Authors and Editors
(in alphabetic order)

Baker, Maria -
ChEss, National Oceanography
Centre, Southampton, United Kingdom

Ebbe, Brigitte -
CeDAMar, Forschungsinstitut
Senckenberg, Germany

Høyer, Jo -
MAR-ECO, Institute of
Marine Research, Norway

Menot, Lenaick -
COMARGE, Institut Océanographique,
Paris & IFREMER, Brest, France

Narayanaswamy, Bhavani -
EuroCoML, Scottish Association for
Marine Science, Oban, United Kingdom

Ramirez-Llodra, Eva -
ChEss, Institut de Ciències del Mar,
CSIC, Spain & NOCS, UK

Steffensen, Morten -
MAR-ECO, Bergen Museum,
University of Bergen, Norway

Contributors

Bernal, Patricio -
Executive Secretary of UNESCO's
Intergovernmental Oceanographic
Commission (IOC)

Boyle, Peter -
MAR-ECO, University of
Aberdeen, United Kingdom

Tyler, Paul -
ChEss, National Oceanography Centre,
Southampton, United Kingdom

© DESEO Editorial Group

Production: Sturla Bang,
Symbolon Forlag, Norway
Design/pre press: Jan Hanchen Michelsen
Printed in EU

ISBN 82-7887-028-4

Deeper than Light

Contents

Please note: Bold outlining of words indicates references to the glossary on page 78.

Front cover: A deep water angler fish, *Haplophryne mollis*. © David Shale. Back cover: The amphipod *Phronima* is a parasite of salps in the North Atlantic. © David Shale

The deep ocean: Discovering an unknown world

Daunted by its huge volume, mysterious due to its relative inaccessibility, the deep ocean continues to fascinate us.

We know that it is there, but we cannot easily visit it. The deep ocean is the largest living space on Earth, but no other part of the biosphere is as poorly explored. Deep ocean research is little more than a hundred years old, much younger than most other science areas, and there are many reasons why this is the case: lack of priority, technology and resources; this is slowly changing. In the last decade, thanks to initiatives such as the global programme the Census of Marine Life (www.coml.org), its national and regional committees such as the European Census of Marine Life (www.eurocoml.org), and its field projects MAR-ECO, ChEss, COMARGE, and CeDA-Mar, we are making huge leaps towards a new and greater understanding of this environment. These international exploratory efforts generate exciting new insights into the biodiversity and ecology of many deepwater habitats from continental slopes to mid-ocean ridges and abyssal plains, using modern technology and vessels.

These efforts are very timely. The international nature management is challenged by global problems such as habitat degradation and biodiversity loss. This also happens or can happen in remote deepwater areas. Preventative actions are needed to stop destructive practices and protect vulnerable habitats and ecosystems still untouched and in near pristine condition. The deep ocean is our common heritage and most open ocean areas are in international waters, i.e. not under the jurisdiction of a single state. Thus international management is required and actions should be based on scientific knowledge and good advice from the international scientific community.

But underlying all exploratory science and effective ocean management is the appreciation of the deep ocean as a fascinating part of our common world. Fascination with nature and its diverse life forms drives ocean scientists to explore this vast environment. Written by scientists actively participating in the projects mentioned above and the project officer for the European Census of Marine Life, and illustrated by images from recent expeditions, this book aims to raise the awareness of everyone to the hidden and beautiful creatures of the deep ocean, how they live and how they are observed and studied. We wish you all a happy voyage "Deeper than Light".

Patricio Bernal
Executive Secretary of UNESCO's Intergovernmental Oceanographic Commission (IOC)

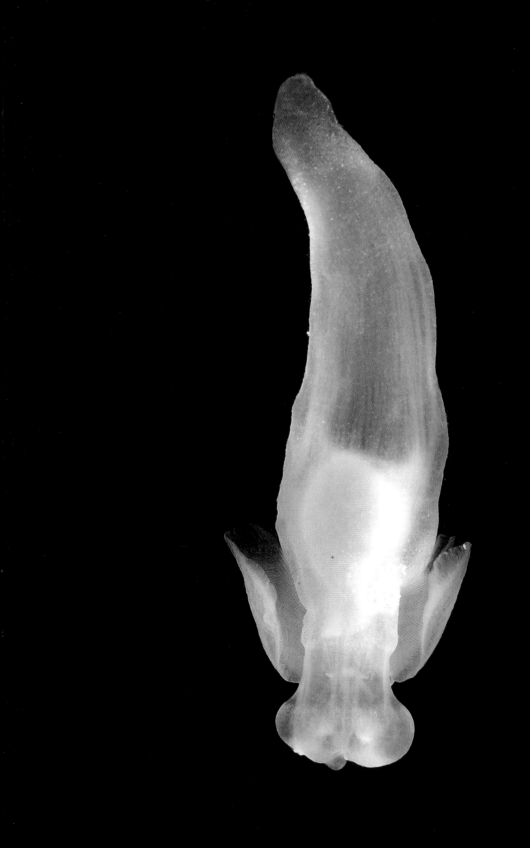

Introduction

Geographical Exploration

The earliest perception of the earth and the sea was that they were flat and if a sailor reached the horizon, he would fall off the edge! The geographical extent of the sea was unknown, its depth unfathomable, and unlikely to be tested as myth proclaimed that the deep waters were inhabited by monsters ready to take the unwary seaman.

Geographical exploration, especially in the 15th and 16th centuries showed that the sea extended far beyond the horizon visible from land. For another three hundred years the surface of the sea continued to be explored as it carried Europeans on great voyages of discovery. By comparison technological development was slow, although notable advances included the accurate measurement of longitude in the 18th century by John Harrison and the development of steam power in the 19th century.

In the great age of geographic exploration the most important feature other than surface geography was the depth of the water particularly in relation to the closeness of land.

The snail, *Clione limacina*, "flying" through the water using its foot which has evolved into two wing-like lobes to be used for propulsion. © David Shale

Sounding lines had been in use from time immemorial to ensure that ships would not run aground. The first description of the 3-dimensional ocean was by soundings laid on a map of the sea in 1504. By 1521, Magellan had attempted to measure the depth of the ocean between the coral islands of St Paul and Los Tiburones, in the Pacific, and having found no bottom with a 600 m sounding line announced he had found the deepest part of the ocean. In the 16th and 17th century a series of apparatus were developed to determine depth. British Royal Navy ships were in the forefront of the establishment of **bathymetry,** and as the great maritime surveys took place in the 18th and 19th centuries, special devices to collect sediment samples were added to the sounding lines to give some idea of seabed composition. The late 18th century saw the deepest depth recorded in the ocean of 1300 m in the Arctic, and a sample of 'blue mud' from the seabed was brought up at the same time. The 19th century culmination of this approach was Maury's bathymetric map of the North Atlantic that, for the first time, showed the ocean seabed was not flat as had been imagined but that there were **abyssal plains** separated by a mountain chain running the length of the Atlantic.

Temperature measurements at depth were first taken on Cook's 1772-1773 voyage to the

FIG. 17.—The Dredging and Sounding Arrangements on board the 'Challenger.'

Scientists and crew preparing sampling equipment during the HMS *Challenger* global expedition (1872-6). © NOAA Photo Library

did you ever meet one,

A fantasy sea monster eyeing up a sailing ship. © Mary Evans Picture Library

Pacific. Later that century saw the development of the protected thermometer and by the mid-1800s there had been the development of the **reversing thermometer** that gave accurate temperature readings at depth.

Biological Exploration: The Heroic Age

It is a sounding line that introduces us to deep sea biology. The Sir John Ross expedition undertook a survey in Baffin Bay, Canada, in 1818 at depths approaching 2000 m. Upon retrieval of the sounding line a large bottom-dwelling basket star **(echinoderm)** was recovered demonstrating that animals could be found at great depths in the ocean. This observation remained unknown by the scientific community for decades! Some 20 years later the great British naturalist Edward Forbes was sampling in the Aegean Sea. The choice was unfortunate as this is one of the more impoverished areas of the deep sea bed. On sampling below 600 m Forbes found no animals, and proposed that little or no life existed below this depth. Although not coined by Forbes, this became known as the **'azoic theory'**.

There is nothing like a theory to challenge scientists! At the same time as Forbes was proposing that there was no life below 600 m, Michael and Georg Ossian Sars, father and son, were sampling in the deep Norwegian fjords and finding rich communities of large animals, demonstrating that animals had the ability to thrive in waters of great depth. In addition, a telegraph cable laid at a depth of 2400 m in the Mediterranean was recovered and found to be covered in corals, **molluscs** and other animals. Other examples of the recovery of deep-water animals followed in quick succession but it was the systematic surveys of Charles Wyville-Thomson that set a new standard.

To determine if deep-water fauna occurred to the west of the British Isles, Wyville-Thomson and W.B. Carpenter of the Royal Society (UK) began to collaborate with the British Royal Navy resulting in the cruise of HMS *Lightning* (1868). Although not primarily biological, the cruise demonstrated the presence of a ridge, between Scotland and the Faroes, separating the Norwegian Sea from the North Atlantic. North of this ridge (now the Scotland-Faroes-Iceland-Greenland Ridge) was known as the 'cold' area (temperatures <5 °C), whilst to the south was the 'warm' area (temperatures 4.5 - 8.5 °C). Further expeditions were undertaken in 1869 and 1870 by Wyville-Thomson and Carpenter on HMS *Porcupine* to sample the Faroe-Shetland area, an area to the west and southwest of Ireland, and the western Mediterranean. At the deepest stations sampled the nets caught and retrieved large marine organisms. The 'azoic theory' was dead.

In continued discussions with the Admiralty, Wyville-Thomson established what became known as the *Challenger* Expedition. The plan was to circumnavigate the global oceans sampling to the greatest depths. This was carried out between 1872 and 1876 and *Challenger* sampled some 362 stations and collected a wide variety of truly deep-sea animals. In addition, the *Challenger* cruise collected data on deep-water temperatures, chemistry and sediment type. The expedition showed that animals could live at the greatest depths and the deep sea appeared to be a refuge or 'hiding-place' for groups such as the stalked crinoids (echinoderms), long thought to be extinct. The *Challenger* Reports can be described as the first chronicle of deep sea biology.

Dolphins following a research vessel. © Leif Nøttestad

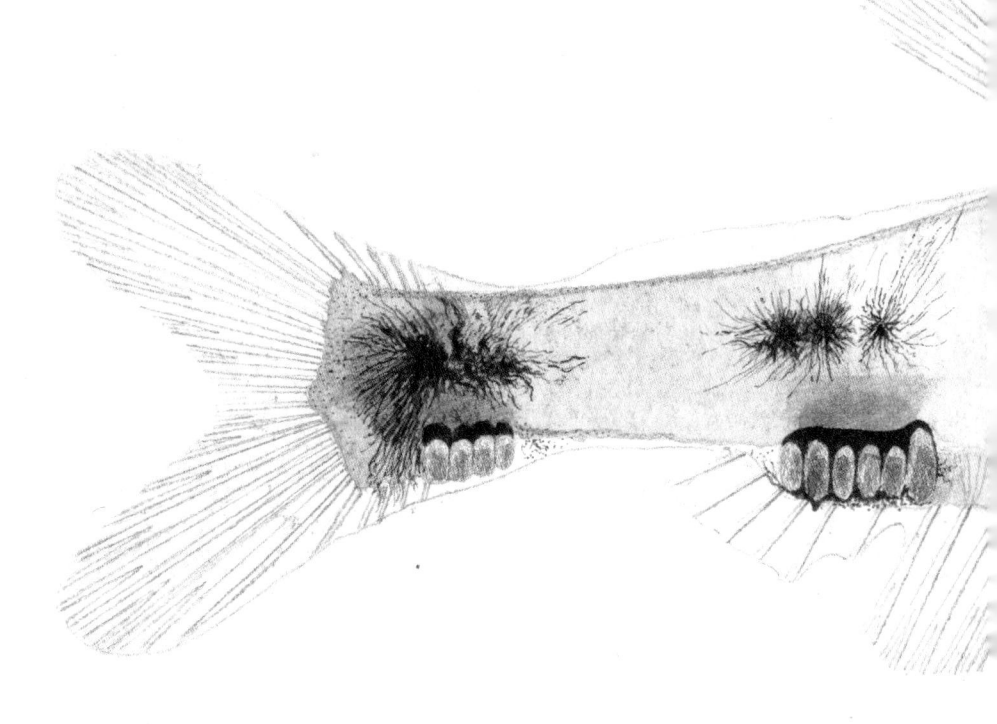

At the same time as the *Challenger* expedition, the US *Tuscarora* was taking physical measurements in the Pacific and the German *Gazelle* was circumnavigating the globe.

Thus interest in organisms found in the deep sea exploded with all the developing nations mounting deep sea expeditions. This has become known as the 'heroic age' of deep-sea exploration with the *Blake* (US) in the Caribbean and Gulf of Mexico and the *Albatross* (US) along the eastern seaboard of the USA.

From the 1880s onwards the various ships of the Prince of Monaco sampled in the Mediterranean and eastern Atlantic, the *Ingolf* (Denmark) sampled along the Wyville-Thomson Ridge and the *Michael Sars* (Norway) in the North Atlantic. In the early part of the 20th century deep sea exploration was eclipsed by the race to either pole and subsequently by the horrors of the Great War. Resource and manpower were being directed to other, more pressing causes.

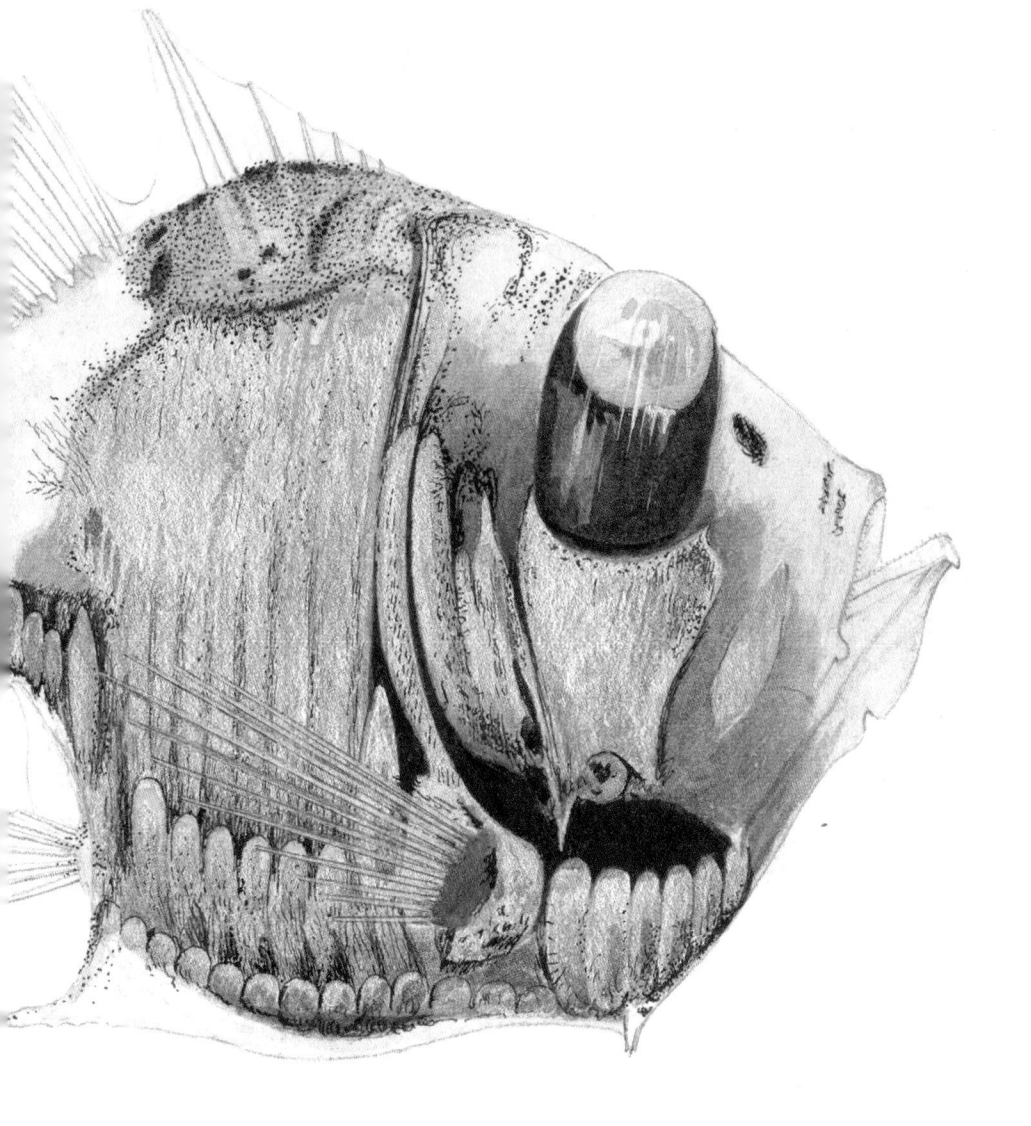

A watercolour of the mid-water hatchet fish, *Argyropelecus hemigymnus*, by Thorolv Rasmussen from 1910 – The *Michael Sars* expedition. © Bergen Museum

By the end of the Great War the impetus of deep sea exploration had been lost and was not regained until the late 1920's and 1930's when the Anglo-Egyptian *Mabahiss* expedition explored the deep parts of the Indian Ocean and the Dutch *Snellius* explored the Dutch East Indies. At the same time the Swedish *Siboga* sampled worldwide, although very few stations were situated in the deep sea. War again intervened leading to a suspension of international research. Immediately after World War

II the Swedes led the *Albatross* expedition of 1947-1948, amongst other places, the Gulf of California. The culmination of this 'heroic age' was the Danish *Galathea* expedition of 1950-1952 that specifically sampled the deepest trenches (>10 000 m) and showed that animals were capable of living in the very deepest parts of the world's oceans. Although the many expeditions over this period collected numerous new species, the equipment used to collect them consisted mainly of coarse mesh trawls and fish traps, and virtually none of it retrieved quantitative samples. As a result the larger animals **(megafauna)** became well known and it was assumed that biodiversity was generally low in the deep sea. It was to be with new equipment and new vigour that the true contributors to biodiversity in the deep sea were to be recognised in the 1960s.

Modern Deep Sea Discovery

In the 1960s a more quantitative approach to sampling deep sea fauna was undertaken by Howard Sanders and Bob Hessler, both then at the Woods Hole Oceanographic Institute (US). They developed a number of dredges and sleds with which to sample deep-sea animals. The significance of these samplers is that they sampled the sediment and retained smaller individuals of the community, known as the **macrofauna**. With careful sieving, using a finer mesh, and sorting of the samples, an astonishing high biodiversity was revealed. Dominant amongst the retained fauna were worms, **crustaceans** and small molluscs suggesting the deep sea may be one of the main repositories of biodiversity on earth.

Running in parallel to deep sea faunal discoveries was an understanding of the processes that maintained deep sea populations. The deep sea is a heterotrophic system, in that it relies on the input of organic matter from surface primary production or from large food falls such as whales, wood and other poten-

The manned submersible MIR-2 being launched. This scientific submersible can carry 3 people to the depths of the ocean (6000 m).
© Klokkargaarden Film AB

Far right: Bizarre new life found at hydrothermal vents in the Pacific Ocean in 1977.
© Emory Kristof (National Geographic Photographer), Richard A. Lutz and Woods Hole Oceanographic Institution

tial food focuses. Since the amount of organic material entering the deep sea is low, the populations were considered small, although diverse.

Further expeditions have led to other fascinating discoveries including the finding of hot water vents in the Eastern Pacific, where black smoke appeared to be emanating from chimneys. The first temperature measurements melted the probes suggesting very high temperatures but even more astounding was the huge biomass of unknown animals associated with these 'hydrothermal vents'. Practically every species was new and biomass was much higher than at equivalent depths in the deep sea.

From mid-ocean ridges to seamounts, from the continental margins out to the abyssal plains, advances in technology and sheer good luck will influence future discoveries in the deep ocean. In the past we relied heavily on dredges and trawls which sampled large areas, making it impossible to discriminate local variation. The use of coring equipment and submersibles, and more recently remotely operated vehicles, has allowed us to study deep sea animals at a much smaller scale, almost as if working on the laboratory bench. Modern molecular techniques allow us to tell the difference between two individuals that look identical but in fact are two closely related species.

Lastly, but by no means least, serendipity will play its part. Hydrothermal vents were an unexpected but fortuitous discovery and of huge importance but there have been many unexpected discoveries in the deep sea on a smaller scale but of no less importance as they contribute to our understanding of this, the world's largest ecosystem.

Many new discoveries are just waiting to be made!

Extreme Ocean Adventure

Join us on an ocean adventure. Our journey begins in relatively shallow waters at the edge of the **continental shelf** (200 m), moving deeper towards the **continental slope** (200 – 3000 m) and then into the deepest, darkest part of the ocean – the abyssal plains (3000 - 6000 m). What interesting deep-sea features will we discover en route?

But be aware, this is going to be an extreme outdoor adventure! Be prepared to experience:

Crushing pressure: As you descend the pressure increases by 1 atmosphere or 1 kg/cm² every 10 m. When you reach the bottom of the abyssal plains, at a depth of 5000 m that is equal to 500 kg/cm², equivalent to the weight of an elephant sitting on you!

Freezing cold: The deep sea is bathed in cold, dense waters coming from Polar Regions. Temperature here can be as low as 0 °C and rarely reaches 4 °C. Train yourself by living in the fridge, do not forget the elephant!

Dimming darkness: Even the clearest waters absorb the sunlight quickly. Below a depth of 200 m you will experience eternal twilight and

The deep sea anglerfish, *Caulophryne* sp. has a spine protruding from its head which acts as a lure to attract prey. © David Shale

A basket star, *Gorgonocephalus sp.,* on top of stony corals, *Lophelia pertusa.* © Ifremer/Caracole cruise 2001.

below 1000 m eternal night. Once you are in the fridge, do not forget to close the door!

Starving hunger: As there is no light, **algae** and plants, the basis of nearly all food chains on Earth, are absent in the deep sea. Seasonal food comes almost solely from small organic particles slowly sinking from the surface, the so-called **marine snow**. Now that you and the elephant are in the dark fridge, there is little room for food except for a few crumbs...You are now ready to experience life in the deep sea!

Sliding Down The Slope

Though conditions are extreme from the human point of view, an amazingly diverse animal life is found in the deep sea. Let us now discover where those animals live and who they are. We begin our journey sliding down what is known as the continental slope.

Mud, Mud Glorious Mud

Continental margins are the ultimate receptacle for most of the sediment generated by land erosion. Mud is therefore a prominent feature of the margins; sediment can be piled as high as 12 km but most life, except bacteria, inhabits the first few centimetres, where the food is found.

Deep sea sediments have long been viewed as a desert, which at first glance is true. Along the slope, the biomass of **benthic organisms** ranges between 10 − 20 g/m², one order of magnitude less than in deserts. Due to its remoteness as well as low numbers, deep sea fauna remained hidden until only half a century ago when scientists began to use new techniques to extract animals from the sediments. Much to their surprise a highly diverse fauna was revealed. Indeed, continental margin sediments later turned out to harbour one of the most diverse ecosystems on Earth; maybe as diverse as tropical rain forests and shallow coral reefs.

Low Oxygen Neighbourhood

While continental margins are basically muddy, food poor and highly diverse environments, there are many exceptions. One example is seafloor oxygen minimum zones (OMZs), especially in the eastern Pacific Ocean and Indian Ocean.

At a global scale, over one million km² of the seafloor, the size of Scandinavia (two times France/Spain, three times Germany, five times United Kingdom), is affected by a permanent shortage in oxygen. Oxygen minimum zones form in the oceans where high surface **productivity** is associated with more or less stagnant and already oxygen poor waters.

The degradation of organic matter in the water column consumes the oxygen until almost depleted. Very few organisms are able to cope with a shortfall of oxygen, therefore when oxygen-depleted waters touch the seafloor they impact and modify the ecosystem. **Diversity** is low but the few species able to live there take advantage of abundant food and low predation to flourish; thanks to special adaptations like highly developed **branchiae**.

Many of these specialised species are new to science and probably **endemic** to oxygen minimum zones.

A large seastar leaves its mark as it wanders over muddy sediments in the deep Norwegian Sea.
© National Oceanography Centre, Southampton

Mayhem On The Slope

Continental margins are not the quiescent areas once imagined. The slopes bordering the continents can suffer catastrophic events; the most impressive catastrophe occurring on the continental slopes are the giant submarine landslides. One of the largest is the *Storegga* suite; three slides whose immense headwall, nearly 300 km long, runs along the edge of the continental shelf off the coast of Norway. The first and most impressive slide occurred 30 000 to 50 000 years ago giving rise to a tsunami on the West coast of Scotland. The slides, together with the last glaciation event, probably caused massive extinctions in the deep Nordic Seas. Since then, recolonisation of the deep Nordic Seas has been slowed by the presence of shallow submarine sills acting as a barrier to dispersal. Even now these continental margins are less diverse than the rest of the North East Atlantic.

Grand Canyons

Canyons are deep incisions of the continental shelf and slope with many different origins, which explain the jagged outline of the European ocean margin. Not all canyons are connected to a river but where they are, they can quickly carry out huge quantities of sediment from the shelf to the abyssal plain. Sediments can also accumulate in the upper to middle

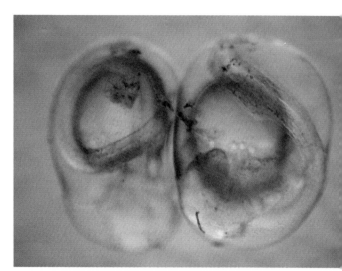

Left: Deep-sea fish eggs with developing embryos. © Anne Stene

Above, right: In the abyssal Pacific Ocean at 5000 m, a sea cucumber, *Psychropotes longicauda*, ingests sediments from around a field of manganese nodules. © Ifremer/ Nodinaut cruise 2004

Above: These sea lilies, *Koehlermetra porrecta*, relatives of sea cucumbers and seastars, gracefully swim to find the best feeding spots. Here they are found at the top of a coral mound situated off Ireland. © Ifremer/Caracole cruise 2001

envious of their shallow water tropical counterparts. Unlike their shallow-water cousins, deep-water corals always lack symbiotic light-dependent algae. Of the 672 species of these non-symbiotic stony corals, about 500 live in deep waters, up to a depth of 6000 m, but only a few of them are able to build large reefs in deep waters. The most common of these reef-building species is *Lophelia pertusa*. Over the last thousand to million years, this species has built giant **carbonate mounds** up to 300 m high and several kilometres in diameter on continental slopes, home to a diverse though fragile ecosystem in the deep sea.

Deep Secret Gardens

Coral reefs on continental margins have been known from the 18th century. It is only recently, due to submersibles, that they have revealed gorgeous sceneries, which have no reason to be

part of the canyon until they collapse creating a **turbidity flow**, which like an avalanche of mud can be devastating. Very few species are likely to survive such events, but in fact little is known regarding the fauna inhabiting active canyons.

The Great Expanse

Timeless And Endless ...

As we walk just a few steps away from the last foothills of the **continental rise**, take a look around and you will most likely be closer to experiencing the stillness of outer space than on any other place on Earth.

We have reached the endless expanse of the abyssal plains, consisting of a very thick blanket of mostly muddy sediments lying, on average, under 4000 - 5000 m of water, smoothing out any roughness of the underlying oceanic crust. The marine snow thins out with very little setting on the seafloor. It amounts to just a few millimetres to centimetres in a millennium; it is rarely disturbed by currents, and is only occasionally stirred up by fish or squid and sometimes human activity. Stones and boulders that have been released from the undersides of the melting icebergs, or rolled down the continental slopes, lie in the same position for tens of thousands of years until we pick them up by chance in our nets or cores.

Most of the Earth's unbroken abyssal plains are in the Atlantic Ocean because it is the quietest ocean as far as volcanic activity is concerned. The largest plain, the Sohm Plain east of

A sea lily, *Anthedon petasus*, fixed on corals spreads its arms in the current to feed on small particles in the water. © Ifremer/Caracole cruise 2001

Newfoundland, is hundreds of kilometres wide, thousands of kilometres long and encompasses an area of approximately 900 000 km². The well-known "ring of fire" surrounding the shores of the Pacific Ocean are responsible for the much greater dynamic conditions seen in this region. Thus the abyssal plain in the Pacific Ocean contains greater amounts of exposed rock compared to the Atlantic.

...But Not So Quiet

The apparent timelessness and endlessness of abyssal plains is only one side of the coin.

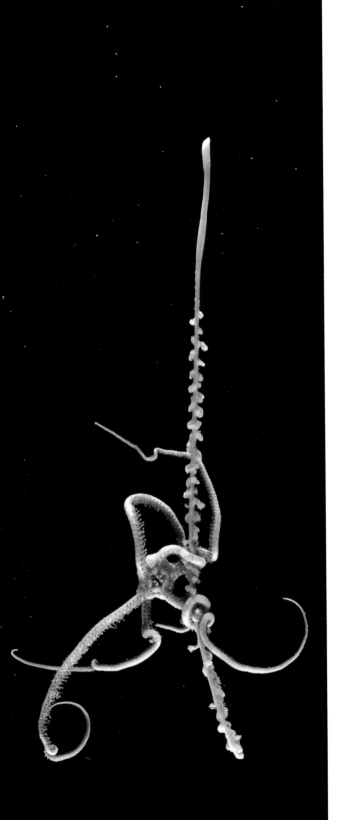

Turn it over, and you will be offered a closer look at this far away world through a magnifying glass. Regardless of having been proven wrong many times about the diversity of life in habitats that are foreign to us, even scientists used to think of the abyssal plains as deserts; practically devoid of life except for the occasional giant squid or bizarre looking fish waiting sluggishly for something edible to come by.

Eternal darkness, the pressure of several hundred atmospheres, a constantly low temperature close to freezing point, and the obvious scarcity of food do not appear very inviting to us.

A brittle star climbs to the top of a sea pen to reach the best position for feeding on passing food particles. © David Shale

We were proven wrong yet again! The wonders of life on the abyssal seafloor take place in the world of the small and very small organisms. The diversity of life here is just as breathtaking as in any other marine environment. Such diversity can only develop if a habitat can somehow be divided among the species inhabiting it. The organisms living in or on the sediments of abyssal plains have managed to do so in a way that is still hidden to us.

Of course there are larger animals too. In fact, the first photographs ever taken in the deep sea, were published in 1971 by Bruce Heezen and Charles Hollister. The photographs showed large animals, all belonging to the echinoderms, mainly sea cucumbers, the somewhat slug-gish cousins of sea stars and sea urchins. They were observed and photographed ploughing through the soft sediment, leaving characteristic trails behind them.

For all abyssal animals, large or small, life is either feast or famine. Over long periods of time, food is scarce because there is no plant life in the absence of light. But the seasons are felt, even down here five kilometres away from the sunlight. When conditions are right far above the seafloor, algae undergo mass developments, turning surface waters green, until the population finally dies as a result of lack of oxygen. Even though it takes several weeks for the dead cells to sink to the deep sea floor, they are perceived as a food pulse by the communities on the seabed, allowing the animals to store enough energy to reproduce, which is energetically a costly affair. Produc-ing eggs and sperm is only the first step; somehow ma-king sure that they get close enough for fertilisation is another, not to mention brooding behaviour that some species exhibit to protect their young from becoming their neighbours' next tasty meal.

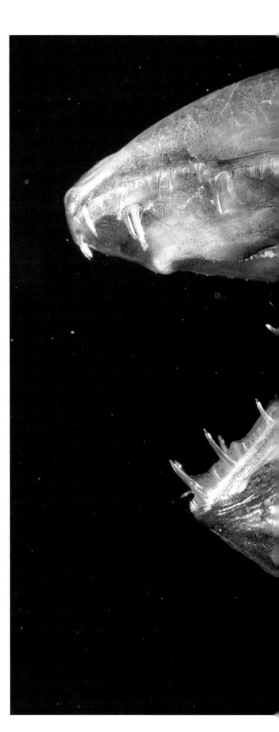

An impressive deep-water fish,
Gonostoma sp. © David Shale

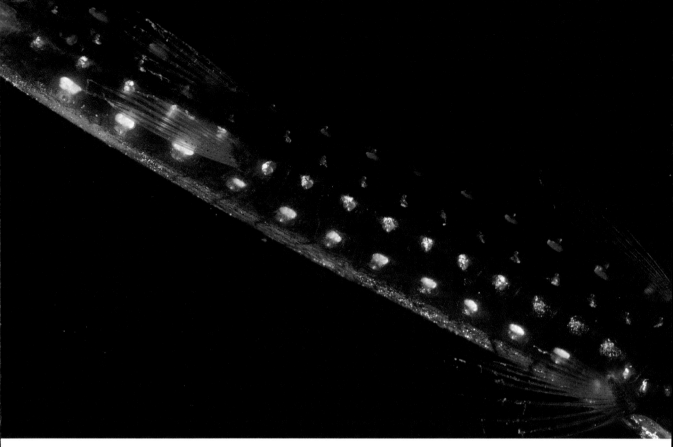

Impressive light organs are found on the body of this fish *Gonostoma* sp. © David Shale

Himalaya In The Deep Sea

We started our gradual descent into the deep sea along the continental margin, taking in numerous different types of habitats: we have crawled through muds dominated by worms, slid carefully down slopes trying not to cause an avalanche, clambered gently over the unexpected yet beautiful deep-water reefs, wandered through what at first glance appears to be an expanse of nothing and have now been stopped in our tracks by a Himalaya in the deep sea.

The Birth Of The Ocean Floor

The longest mountain ranges in the world exist in the depths of our oceans. At approximately 60 000 km in length and in some places more than 800 km wide, they are certainly impressive! These underwater mountain chains, known as mid-ocean ridge systems, are being created where the Earth's

The keen eye of a cephalopod,
Gonatus steenstrupi. © David Shale

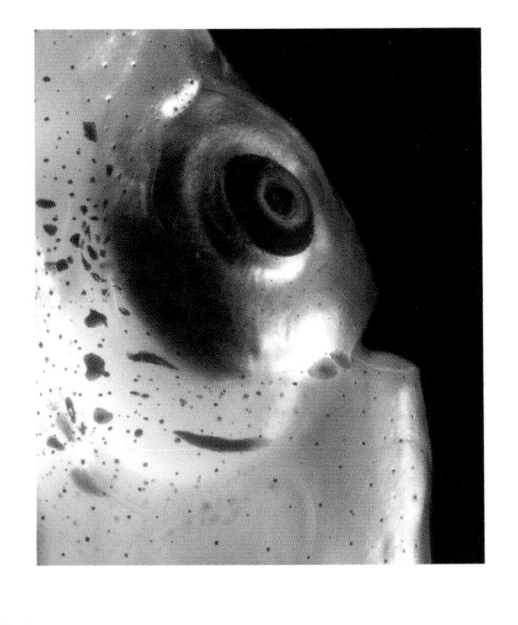

tectonic plates are being pulled apart. New **magma** is constantly emerging onto the ocean floor at the ridge axes and as it crystallises, it forms new crust (basalt and gabbro). The rate at which a mid-ocean ridge creates new material is known as the spreading rate, and is generally measured in millimetres per year. These rates can very from ~10 mm/yr to over 100 mm/yr, depending upon location.

It is truly amazing that we knew little of their existence before 1950! These massive

A large deep-water octopus, *Benthoctopus* sp. © David Shale

A sea urchin makes tracks on the deep sea bed. © National Oceanography Centre, Southampton

ridge systems which wind their way between our continents lay undiscovered until a team of scientists led by Marie Tharp and Bruce Heezen discovered an enormous mountain chain running along the middle of the Atlantic Ocean.

It was initially thought that this phenomenon was only to be found in the Atlantic. However, data gathered by oceanographic surveys conducted by many nations over the next few years led to the discovery that every ocean contained parts of the ridge system and that they joined up to form this spectacular geological formation.

Mid-ocean ridges are dynamic environments and are literally renewing the surface of our planet. Thousands of volcanoes and volcanic ridge segments are found on the ridge and indeed, some of the most active volcanoes on Earth exist here – eruptions are frequent. Occasionally the ridge breaks the surface of the ocean to form islands; examples of these are Iceland and the Azores in the Atlantic. The landscape (topography) of a mid-ocean ridge consists of numerous rugged hills, rising on average to about 4000 m above the sea floor, valleys, and deep fracture zones, the deepest of which can be more than 4000 m deep.

The Ridge Snack-Bar

The mid-ocean ridges have recently been discovered to house a much higher level of animal diversity than previously thought. Some of the reasons given are the high levels of productivity found around these ridges, a similar phenomenon seen around many seamounts. So why is productivity at these ridges so high when they are so far from land? After all there is no input of terrestrial nutrients and organic matter to these regions. The complex topography of the mid-ocean ridges strongly influences the **hydrography**, including the pathways of deep-water oceanic currents and water masses. As a result deep cold water containing lots of nutrients is sometimes forced

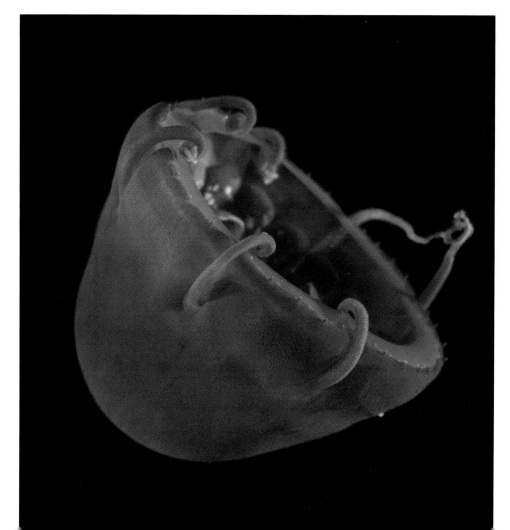

A 4 cm wide jellyfish, Aeginura grimaldii, collected from 900 m depth over the Mid-Atlantic Ridge. © David Shale

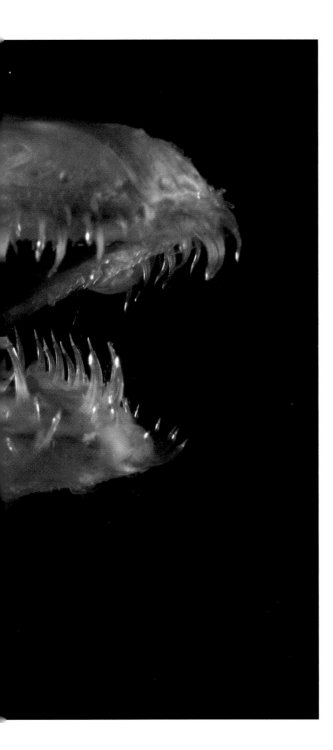

This lizard fish, *Bathysaurus ferox*, is an ambush predator often observed resting on the seabed. © David Shale

upwards towards the surface of the ocean providing increased nutrients allowing for the explosion in biological production, in particular the growth of algae, the plants of the ocean. Feeding on the algae are other small animals and in turn they are preyed upon by larger animals. Production increases up the **trophic** levels.

Mid-ocean ridges act as vertical ladders for the movement and mixing of animals throughout the full depth of the ocean. Biological production in the surface layer may be elevated around seamounts and ridges compared with the much deeper adjacent ocean basins. Scientists have for example thought of deep sea **pelagic** fish as nomadic wanderers, but recent studies along the Mid-Atlantic Ridge gives evidence that deep sea pelagic fish are more closely associated with the topography of the ridge, and that these fish are congregating at the ridge, ready for spawning.

Animals such as whales also appear to seek out such areas of high food abundance. Many of these "snack bars" also happen to coincide with the migration routes of whales and dolphins. In the Atlantic, an example of these are areas of the Mid-Atlantic Ridge between Iceland and the Azores. It seems to be a favoured migration route of some of the large whales.

The first black smokers discovered on the south section of the Mid-Atlantic Ridge, 2005.

© University of Bremen

Deep Chemical World

As we traverse the mid-ocean ridge we are shocked when we stumble into hot water... literally!!

Black Smokers

1977 was the year of a major discovery that would change our understanding of life on our planet: an extraordinary landscape of underwater volcanoes – called hydrothermal vents – and new bizarre animals were found.

Vents are found on volcanic mountain ranges, called mid-ocean ridges. In these dramatic regions where tectonic plates are being pulled apart and new seafloor is being created, cold seawater (2 °C) penetrates **the ocean crust** and is heated to temperatures as high as 400 °C. This super-heated water, known as **hydrothermal fluid**, rises back to the seafloor

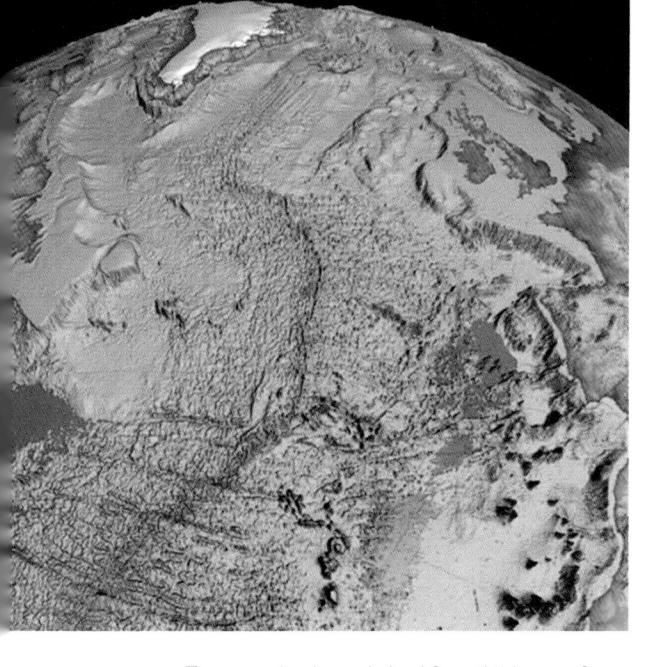

The ocean has been drained from this image of the Earth to reveal the northern portion of the Mid-Atlantic Ridge, which extends from pole to pole. © DLR and Nils Sparwasser

A computer generated image of the mid-ocean ridge system. © NRK

having lost all its oxygen and now is full of chemical compounds and dissolved metals. The fluid is spewed out back into the cold deep ocean where the metals come out of solution. The shimmering fluid looks like dense, black smoke coming out of chimneys which may be as tall as houses: the **black smokers!**

The vast majority of life on Earth relies directly or indirectly upon energy produced from the sun. This solar energy is used by plants, algae and some bacteria for the production of organic matter via a process called **photosynthesis**. This may then be used as food to sustain life forms ranging from bacteria to blue whales! Finding thriving communities of animals on the vents was really surprising, as the environmental conditions are extreme for life as we know it. The temperature varies from 2 °C to 400 °C in only a few centimetres! Some of the chemicals

(methane and hydrogen sulphide) and metals found in the vent fluids are highly toxic. Surprisingly though, it is these same chemicals that provide the necessary energy needed for the development of such exotic life in the absence of sunlight. The vents are inhabited by micro-organisms, like bacteria, that use the energy of the chemicals to produce organic matter through a process called **chemosynthesis** as opposed to photosynthesis. These bacteria live free on the seafloor, forming large bacterial mats which are visible to the human eye! They are also found living with large animals in a mutually beneficial relationship (symbiosis) where the animal provides the necessary chemicals and in return the bacteria provide the newly formed organic matter for food. This relationship is the most important adaptation in the vent ecosystem and is responsible for the very high densities of animals on and around vents. These are the oases of the deep oceans! An explosion of life, but the number of different species is actually low, and is a characteristic of ecosystems with extreme environmental conditions.

Since the discovery of vents, hundreds of new species with interesting adaptations have been described. Take a submersible ride to the East Pacific vents and you will find giant tubeworms *(Riftia pachyptila)* that do not have a mouth or gut, feeding only from their symbiotic bacteria. Or you could see a group of smaller but just as fascinating worms *(Alvinella pompejana)*, called the Pompeii worm because they live in tubes on active chimneys where the fluid can be, for short periods of time, as hot as 60 °C! Travelling south, you could come across Yeti crabs *(Kiwa hirsuta)*,

An oasis of life on an East Pacific Rise hydrothermal vent, with giant tubeworms, mussels, vent crabs, snails and a fish.
© E. Kristof (National Geographic Photographer), Richard A. Lutz and Woods Hole Oceanographic Institution

a beautiful white crab with long hairy legs and arms! Change oceans now to the Atlantic, and from the submersible porthole the scene is very different. Thousands of shrimp (*Rimi-caris exoculata*) cover the walls of the black smokers. They do not have eyes, but a modified organ, very sensitive to the low **radiation** of vents, which allows them to move around without getting burnt!

Deep-Sea Champagne

Hydrothermal vents are not the only deep sea ecosystem sustained by chemicals. Cold fluid, laden with hydrogen sulphide, methane and other hydrocarbons, seeps and bubbles through the sediment in certain areas on continental margins. In 1984, dense communities of golden mussels and white and red tube-

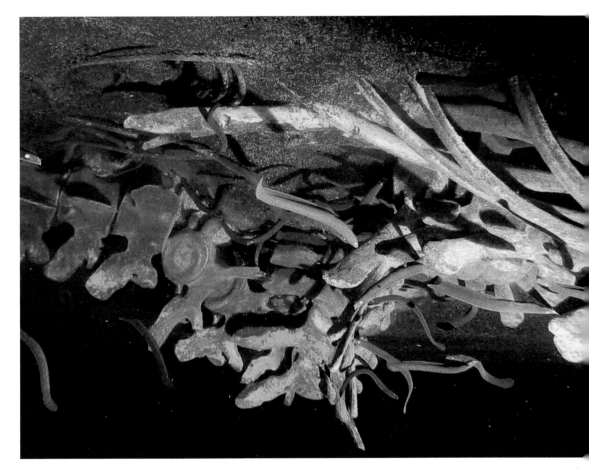

A bacterial oasis forms on whale bones. © Craig Smith, University of Hawaii

worms were found for the first time on **cold seeps** in the Gulf of Mexico. Since then, similar habitats and striking animals have been discovered all around the globe, at depths between a few hundred to a few thousand metres.

Tubeworm bushes from the Gulf of Mexico cold seeps. © Charles Fisher, Penn State University

Fatty Bones

Five years on, further exciting discoveries were made…**whale falls!** In 1989, a whale skeleton was found, by chance, on the Pacific

For over four years, the bones of this 35 ton grey whale have been on the bacteria. © Craig Smith, University of Hawaii

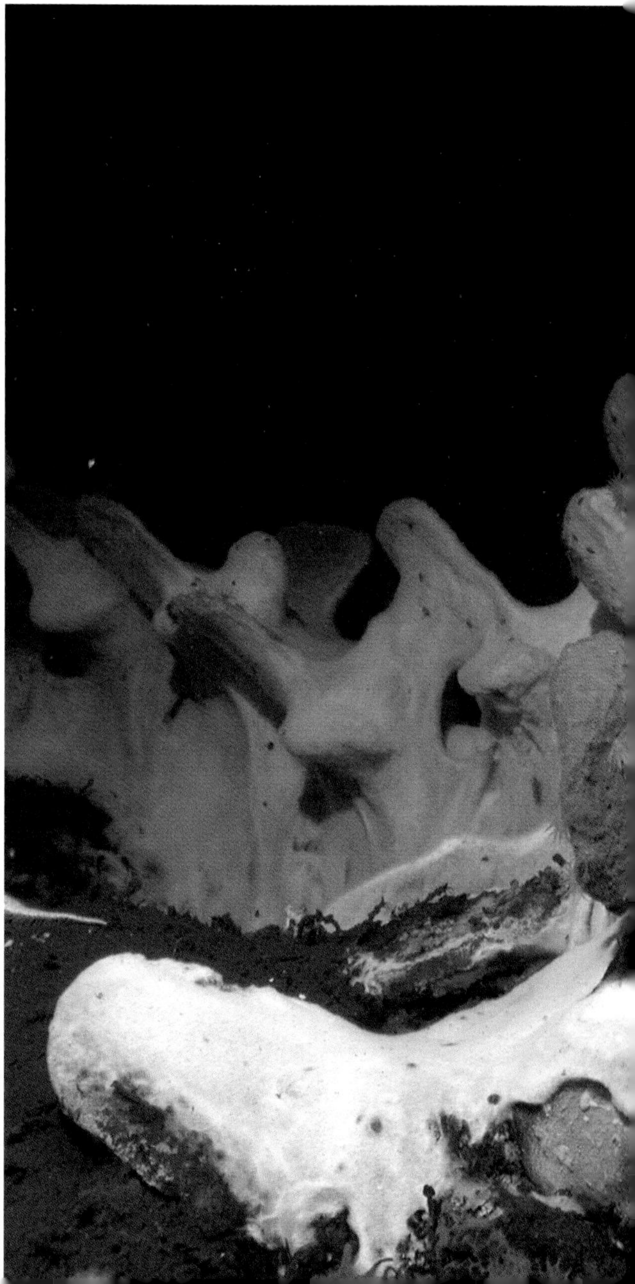

Ocean seafloor. When the scientists analysed the bones in the laboratory, they found chemosynthetic bacteria and associated animals which had adaptations similar to those found on vents and seeps. Since then, many studies have shown that the high concentrations of fats (lipids) in whale bones are broken down by bacteria producing chemicals such as hydrogen sulphide, which is the base for a chemosynthetic-based ecosystem.

...bed and are now covered with thick mats of chemical-loving

Artistic impression of the "Yeti crab" – a new species found at hydrothermal vents on the Easter Island microplate in 2005. Artist: Raymond Cowling, © ChEss

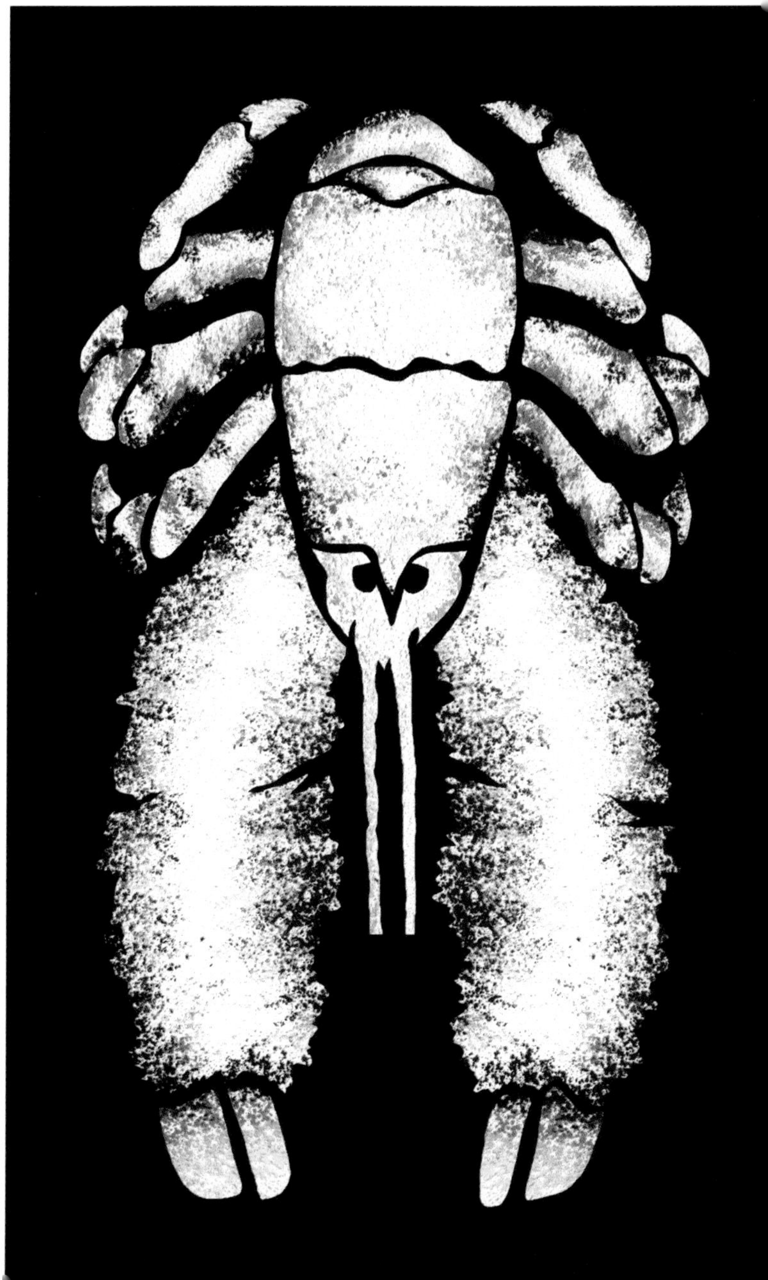

Free Fall From The Surface

Having tumbled down the continental slope and margin, walked on the flat abyssal plain, hauled ourselves over mountains and gazed in awe at billowing black smoke we suddenly wonder what is above us. It is now time to discover the animals and plants living in the water column.

Touched By The Sun - Down To 200 m

Almost all organisms of the oceans ultimately depend on the organic matter produced in this sunlit surface layer.

Plankton have limited mobility and must drift wherever the currents take them. Most are microscopic organisms and plants, but some are very big indeed, such as jellyfish, with tentacles longer than 30 m, and giant colonial animals such as **pyrosomes** that form tubes that even a diver can swim through!

Phytoplankton, the plants of the ocean, are eaten by small drifting organisms namely

A crustacean of the family of Lophogastrida, species *Gnathophausia zoea.* © David Shale

zooplankton. Plant-eating zooplankton come from many different groups, but the copepods which are mm-sized crustacean, can really be regarded as the "cow or antelope of the oceans".

Big crustaceans such as shrimps, krill and amphipods, and a wide range of **gelatinous** zooplankton prey on the plant-eating zooplankton such as copepods. In turn these larger carnivores are consumed by schooling surface fish, cephalopods, baleen whales and even birds.

At high latitudes the surface waters are important nurseries for the floating eggs and

larvae of some deep-living fishes as well as being inhabited by super-abundant small schooling plankton-eating fish. In the North Atlantic, typical species include herring, mackerel, capelin, and blue whiting. At low latitudes, zooplankton density is lower; therefore the abundance of schooling surface fish decreases.

Large fish such as high-speed tunas, billfish, and sharks migrate vast distances and roam the surface ocean waters.

Whales are mammals which comprise animals from dolphins and porpoises to the baleen whales. Strangely, the baleen whales

A majestic red octopus, *Stauroteuthis syrtensis*, found at depths ranging from 500 – 4000 m. © David Shale

such as the blue whale at 33 m in length are the largest vertebrates on the planet, yet they eat by filtering tiny zooplankton from the water. The same is true for the world's two largest fishes, the whale shark and the basking shark. Toothed whales, which are generally smaller, prey mainly on fish and squid. The sperm whale, with its massive head and long lower jaw is an example of a toothed whale and hunts for squid and fish as deep as 2000 m.

Twilight Zone – Between 200 - 1000 m Depth

As we descend deeper and deeper the intensity of the sunlight gradually decreases with little left below 200 m. Animals below this depth experience an "eternal twilight". Many mid-water fishes migrate spectacular distances from their daytime depth of up to 1000 m to the surface layers at night, where they feed

Below: A squid showing off in the lights given off by the submersible from where this photograph was taken. © David Shale

A large shark investigates bait attached to scientific experimental equipment. © OCEANLAB, University of Aberdeen.

on zooplankton. Even small crustaceans mi-grate several hundred metres to graze on phyto-plankton or smaller animals in the shallower depths. At night they are more difficult to spot by visual predators such as surface-dwel-ling fishes, birds and whales. This massive **diurnal migration** happening in all oceans is a primary mechanism for transport of matter and energy into the deep sea. Many of the migrators are red, silvery or black; colours that make them quite invisible at low light levels. Many also have rows of light organs along their underside. When they "turn their lights on" it is difficult for predators to see them against the background of the lighter surface waters.

Gelatinous plankton such as jellyfish, comb-jellies, sea butterflies and arrow worms consist mainly of water and are often transparent, ma-king them almost invisible to predators. They are among the most beautiful and stunning organisms of the sea.

The majority of crustaceans living in the marine environment are hard to see in the dim blue light as many of them are red in colour. The most common are shrimps, krill, amphi-pods and copepods, many of which take part in the never-ceasing diurnal vertical migration cycle. The slogan is "eat and grow, but avoid being eaten", and many adaptations to avoid predators are remarkable. For example, some of the shrimps can create great clouds of light (bioluminescence) to blind potential preda-tors.

This deep-water Oreo, *Neocyttus* sp., inhabits rocky areas of seamounts and hills. © David Shale

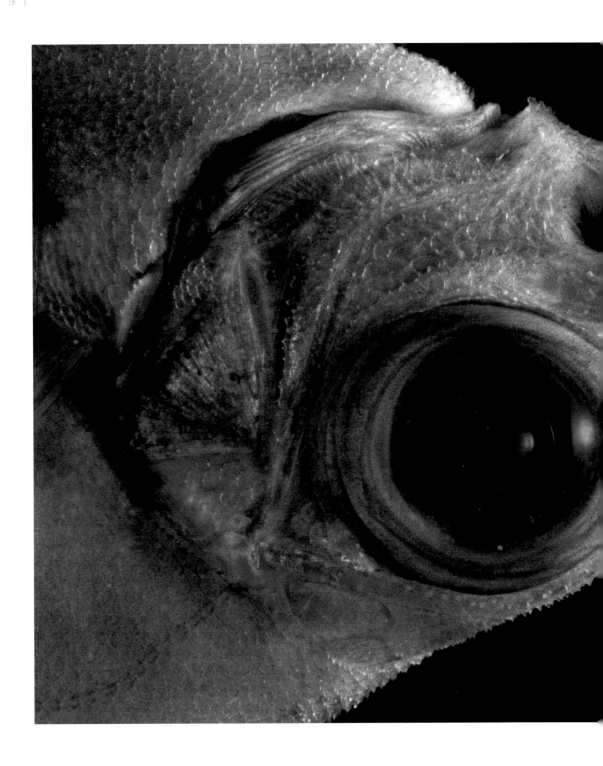

Deeper Than Light –
Below 1000 m

Finally we reach the dark zone, the greatest living space in the ocean. Any light that is present here is produced solely by **bioluminescent** organisms. The water is uniformly cold, currents are generally slower and the pressure is huge. At 1000 m the pressure is about 100 times greater than the pressure at the surface.

Deep sea organisms have therefore evolved special biochemical adaptations to enable them to cope with the elevated pressure. Even with a reduced food input at this depth, the dark zone has a rich diversity of drifting organisms. In the dark zone we find fishes with the weirdest adaptations to low food concentration. Deep sea anglerfish have strange protrusions projecting from their heads; these are either sense organs or "fishing

The eye of a deep-sea squid is one of the most highly developed organs found in the marine world.

rod". The tip of the modified first ray of the dorsal fin is an elaborate bioluminescent lure used to attract prey. Another unusual animal is the pelican eel; like the pelican bird, they have huge expandable mouths that they keep open almost as an inside-out umbrella in order to catch the rare prey.

Cephalopods have roamed all the world's oceans and all depths for more than 450 million years. All are carnivorous, preying on fishes, crustaceans and other cephalopods. They are also important prey items for larger fishes, whales, seals and seabirds. The deep-water cephalopods are particularly poorly known and new species are steadily being discovered. Octopods may swim by jet propulsion, by undulating interconnected tentacles and by fins. A long-armed squid reaching at least 3-4 m in length and displaying beautiful undulating wide fins was only recently filmed.

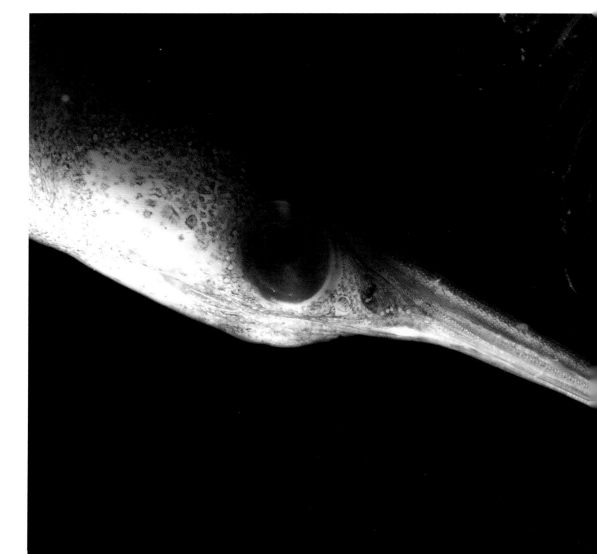

The head of a snipe eel. © David Shale

Glimpses Of The Deep

Now that you have been on your extreme ocean adventure, why not take a glimpse into the deep sea to find out more. Here follows a selection of fascinating snap shots of what lies beneath…

Reefs In The Dark

Let us go back about 10 000 years, to the end of the last **glacial era**. At that time, deep waters began to warm up; deep currents strengthened and hard **substrata** once buried under glacial deposits were exposed. This was the right time for cold stony corals to settle and grow in deep northern European waters, as they did repeatedly, during each interglacial era, for millions of years. Since then, some of these pioneers have built giant coral reefs. The largest one found was discovered in 2002, the Røst reef off Norway, and covers a total area of 100 km².

Colonies of the species *Lophelia pertusa* are the backbone of these reefs in the North-East Atlantic. Such colonies are made up of thousands of individuals called polyps, each of them sheltered in a skeleton. An individual colony builds up by budding, which means that polyps

Sitting on top of a nodule, raising its arms, this sea star *(Freyella sp.)* does its utmost to collect food at 5000 m water depth in the abyssal Pacific.
© Ifremer/Nodinaut cruise 2004

Comb jellies are very common in the deep sea. This one, *Bolinopsis infundibulum*, is exhibiting the wonder of bioluminescence. © David Shale

A gluttonous solitary coral, *Desmophyllum cristagalli*, feeds upon a fish, *Cyclothone* sp., from the Santa Maria di Leuca bank off Italy. © RV Meteor M70/1, Erlangen

A fragment of a colony of the reef-building species *Lophelia pertusa*. The inset shows a close up of an individual polyp. © Ifremer/Caracole cruise 2001

clone themselves. Their clones grow next to them, eventually forming a coral shrub. A colony is either male or female. New colonies are formed by sexual reproduction, the encounter between sperm and eggs hopefully ends up with larvae released in the sea, drifting with, and spread by currents. Some coral patches, the size of a basketball court and 1.5 m high, might have developed by the cloning of a single polyp, whose larvae once settled thousands of years ago. The tangle of white to yellow *Lophelia* shrubs harbours a variety of other, more delicate corals, which all benefit from this projection to literally fish for their food. Using their tentacles, they can poison live prey, which range in size from zooplankton to small fish.

Of Sponges And Worms

When one lives on the seafloor, places to hide are a precious commodity. Predators are able to attack you from all angles. If you are an animal that is able to burrow into the sediment, you can quite easily and quickly disappear. However, there are many animals such as small crustaceans, with legs and antennae ten times longer than their bodies that are much too delicate and therefore unable to penetrate the mud. Any suitable shelter is therefore most welcome, but is extremely hard to come by on the abyssal plains. The additional advantage of having a sheltering structure that extends above the surface of the sediment is their ability to trap sediment and food particles on the down-flow side, much like sand on the beach piling up behind sticks and stones. Whilst exploring the distribution of small sponges on the deep sea floor, scientists found that even a tiny single sponge can provide refuge for small threadlike worms, the **nematodes**, living in the soft sediment layers, giving structure to a seemingly endless expanse. Even the smallest amount of sponge **spicules**, the skeletal

A tangle of corals (*Lophelia pertusa* and *Madrepora oculata*), sponges, sea stars and sea urchins.
© Ifremer/Caracole cruise 2001

The North Atlantic Ocean. The rugged Mid-Atlantic Ridge rises from the deep ocean floor as a gigantic mountain chain. © IMR

remains of dead sponges, can influence the abundance of animals living in the surrounding sediment. The spicules may even be the single most important cause for variability seen in faunal abundance. These patches of sponges and sponge spicules trap organic particles and so provide a food source for the nematodes, which are not thought to have a selective diet.

Finding New Species On The Mid-Atlantic Ridge

Only a tiny fraction of deep sea habitats have been sampled to date, so scientists expected to find new species and even new genera or families during a major expedition to the Mid-Atlantic Ridge in 2004. During the expedition they were amazed at quite how many species they did not recognise and were new to science;

for example 20 % of the deep-water fishes observed were new discoveries in this area of the Atlantic. During the two-month expedition, researchers collected a huge number of animals – in total 80 000 - and of these, 60 000 were fishes. High species diversity was also encountered from many different faunal groups; fishes, cephalopods, bottom-dwelling invertebrates, plankton, fish parasites, marine mammals and seabirds. Images and video footage helped resolve a mystery surrounding an unidentified worm-like creature that turned out to be a new family. As scientists have time to examine the material closely, it is quite possible that they will find more new and exciting species. Describing new species is a task for taxonomists. However, **taxonomy** is time-consuming and there are stringent rules that

Page 48-49: This imposing-looking fangtooth fish, *Anoplogaster cornuta,* will actually fit in the palm of your hand! © David Shale

have to be followed when describing a new species. The descriptions are not valid before a formal publication has been issued and a name has been accepted; all this takes time.

Gutless Worms!

Hydrothermal vents in the Pacific Ocean are home to one of the most astonishing creatu-res on Earth - the giant tubeworm, (meaning the thick feathered vent worm!). These giant worms can reach up to 1.5 metres long and may be as thick as a mans wrist - particularly amazing considering that when they are adults they have no mouth, stomach, intes-tine or anus! The worms live inside white tubes made out of a tough material called chitin.

As adults, giant tubeworms survive only as

A community of giant tubeworms, from the East Pacific hydrothermal vents showing off their beautiful bright red blood-filled plumes © Ifremer/Phare cruise 2002

A microbial reef that uses methane as a source of energy in the Black Sea.
© Antje Boetius, MARUM/Microhab

a result of the close relationship they have with bacteria. These bacteria enter the animal while it is still a juvenile through their primitive mouth and gut. As the worm matures, the mouth and gut disappear, trapping the bacteria inside the body cavity. The worms have a bright red plume of gills that poke out from the top of the tube. The blood-filled plume has the ability to take up oxygen, carbon dioxide and hydrogen sulphide from the cocktail mixture of seawater and vent fluid. The worm then transports these ingredients in its blood to a region called the **trophosome**. The trophosome is home to the billions of bacteria that act to sustain the life of the worm; these bacteria make up to about half the worm's weight! They use the ingredients to manufacture food in the form of organic carbon that nourishes both the bacteria and the giant tubeworm *(Riftia pachyptila)*.

A proposed new species of deep-sea eelpout, genus *Lycodonus*. © Peter Rask Møller

A zoarcid fish swims over a community of the giant tubeworm, *Riftia pachyptila*, on an East Pacific Rise hydrothermal vent. © E. Kristof (National Geographic Photographer), R.A. Lutz and Woods Hole Oceanographic Institution

The Elusive Tube-Builders

Many of the animals living in abyssal sediments consist of only a single cell. Some of them protect the delicate cytoplasm surrounding the **nucleus** with shells, also called tests, which they build either out of substances that they produce themselves or out of sand and mud grains. These tests can be very solid, which makes it impossible to extract the animal from it to study.

A large group of unicellular organisms go by the strange name **Komokiacea,** Komokis for short. Their cytoplasm is strung out into a network of very fine extremities that are coated by tubules of sediment. In the spaces among the tubules, some species accumulate loose mud, resulting in shiny, drop-shaped or beadlike mudballs. Because of their unspectacular looks they have been overlooked for an inordinately long time, and to this day nobody has ever seen the cell itself. Recently, molecular geneticists tried to find out with modern methods just who the Komokis are related to. However, when they looked at the genes they found a whole cocktail of them, all belonging to other animals who apparently use the tubules as shelter. So even now we are still not quite sure who Komokis are related to, maybe sponges or another very common group of one-called animals called **foraminiferans.** The generous tiny builder of the "little balls" continues to remain elusive, having proven resistant to even the most advanced methods in biology.

Mysterious Bacteria

If the 20th century was marked by the discovery of high diversity in the deep sea, the 21st century is possibly going to be marked by the recent discovery of a deep **biosphere;** that is to say bacteria in sediments living as deep as a thousand meters below the seafloor. This is a major discovery; in fact this deep biosphere may comprise a tenth of Earth's living bio-

Unusual bone-eating worms on whale bones found on the Japanese deep-sea floor. © Yoshi Fujiwara, JAMSTEC

mass. A striking feature of these bacteria is how they manage to feed and duplicate in deep sediments that are millions of years old. Scientists suggest that they may be able to fast for years, similar to a very long hibernation and that the community only duplicates once every 1000 years; something that scientists still cannot explain. Others suggest that the bacteria are in fact fuelled by some kind of radioactivity. Some of those strange organisms may also convert CO_2, the main greenhouse gas, into methane, a useful combustible, which already fuels chemosynthetic ecosystems where it leaks from deep sediments to the deep sea floor. Incidentally, large reserves of methane are known to lie below the seabed of the mysterious Bermuda Triangle. One theory now suggests that large leakages of gas might cause instability of the sea and an explosive mixture of air and methane above, enough for a ship or plane travelling over it to sink or burn. Between sustainable energy and piracy, the deep biosphere still has the capability to amaze us.

From Whales To Bone-Eating Worms!

A popular myth says that elderly elephants go to a special place at the end of their lives to die – the elephant graveyard. When a whale dies, it sinks to the depths of the ocean... a whale graveyard? There, it becomes part of the food chain and in an environment where food is scarce, it suddenly provides a feast! First to arrive are the scavengers, such as eel fish and crabs, which devour most of the flesh within months. They are followed by opportunistic worms and small crustaceans that thrive around the skeleton.

Finally, it is the turn of bacteria that break down the fats in the bones, producing sulphides. These chemicals are the energy source that then sustains the establishment of new animal communities. However, bacteria are not the only organisms to feed on the succulent lipids…

In 2004, a little worm called *Osedax*, or the zombie worm, was found on the skeleton of a grey whale in the Pacific. These worms, the size of a finger, have long roots on one end and beautiful red and white 'feathers' on the other. The roots penetrate the whale bones and are associated with bacteria that help digest the fats in the bones. The red 'feathers' are full of **haemoglobin** used for the transfer of oxygen from seawater to the animal and bacteria. Surprisingly, the worms seen on the whale skeletons are always females. The males never reach the bones, because, although attaining sexual maturity, they remain microscopic and live inside the females!

The History Book Of The Deep Sea

Think of a starry sky on a still, cold winter's night and it seems to be the most peaceful place imaginable. A first glimpse of the deep sea and you also think how unbelievably tranquil and calm it is. However, if you look at time scales which are much longer than our lifetimes, the starry night is really a lively, vibrant environment, much like the deep sea which can be highly changeable and dynamic, although this can occur within our lifetimes; very different to the initial picture that we see.

Every so often, and probably much more often than we realise, giant avalanches of sediment roll down the steep slopes taking with them not only the usual fine-grained clay, but also quite coarse sand. If you were to cut out a piece of the abyssal sea floor, a bit like cutting a slice of cake with many fillings, you

The deep-water amphipod crustacean, *Megalanceola stephenseni*. © David Shale

column.

would be surprised to see the number of layers of sediments of different grain sizes and colour. This is like a history book reporting on events of long ago. The origin of the sediment layers from the upper parts of the continental slope can be detected by the presence of millions of shells once made by shallow-water one-celled animals, such as the foraminiferans. In other layers, we also find shells (also called tests) of deep-water **protists** surrounded by very fine clay which have slowly settled through the water column.

Anemones from the Lau Basin hydrothermal vent region in the Western Pacific.
© Charles Fisher, Penn State University

Deep Love Stories

Many marine animals produce offspring by releasing (spawning) large quantities of sperm and eggs in to the water column where fertilisation happens. This sounds easier than it is! Sperm and eggs quickly drift away from each other in the currents. However, when successful, embryos develop into microscopic larvae that are transported by the currents until they find a suitable home for settlement. In the deep sea, this is even more challenging... It is not always easy to find a mate when you are

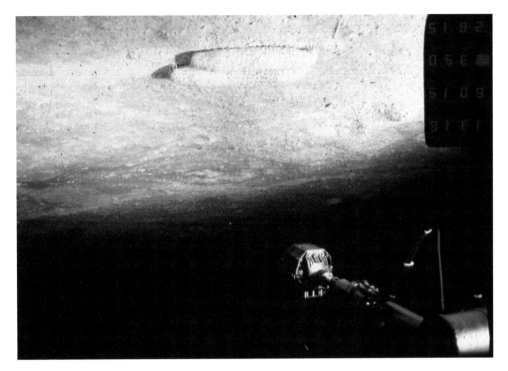

A pair of sea cucumbers find each other on the vast abyssal plains.
© Paul Tyler, National Oceanography Centre, Southampton

wandering around the vast expanse of the deep sea floor. To overcome this problem, some animals have developed interesting behaviour patterns. For example, sea cucumbers and sea urchins have been seen walking in pairs or herds around the deep sea floor. They cannot tell the sex of the individual next to them but when one starts spawning it may trigger the spawning of the rest....party time! By moving in groups, they increase the chances of their eggs and sperm finding each other. Other animals such as some worms, molluscs, crustaceans and fish have even more weird ways of ensuring they produce their next generation. The females of some species have normal-sized adult bodies...but the males are dwarfs, just a fraction of the female size, that attach to the females, their only role to produce sperm!

Earth's Hidden Diversity

Once upon a time, nearly 4 billion years ago, life appeared in the Ocean. During the following 3.5 billion years, life evolved solely in the seas. While the first plants invaded the land about 440 million years ago, almost all marine forms of life, including vertebrates, already existed. Today, most **phyla** are only found in the seas, which cover two thirds of our planet. Of the 1.7 million species currently described, one million are insects but only 230 000 have been described from the marine environment and this is despite the overwhelming supremacy of sea over land. How can such a discrepancy be explained? Are the insects exceptionally gifted in terms of evolution or is there a hidden diversity in the ocean? Indeed hidden marine diversity may well lie in the deep oceans.

One of the most extensive studies undertaken on continental slopes suggests that over 10 million species may inhabit the deep sea floor even although the samples are equivalent to just 21 m^2 of mud. This estimation is controversial but it has the merit of highlighting how poorly known the deep sea ecosystem actually is. What is certain is that new species in the deep sea are collected at a much faster rate than the current ability of scientists to name them.

Light In Darkness

Below 1000 m all visible light disappears; here exists a twilight realm where organisms live in darkness, but are not completely without light. Bioluminescence is a visible light made by living creatures. It is the result of a highly efficient chemical reaction involving an enzyme called luciferase and a substrate called luciferin. The phenomenon is used by many organisms living in the deep sea.

Bioluminescent light has many functions. It can be used as camouflage, as a flashlight, for defence or to attract a mate. In the twilight depths the silhouette of an animal can be seen from below against the dim blue light filtering from above making it an easy target for predators. In order to camouflage themselves, some organisms emit light from their underside which they can control to make a perfect match in colour and intensity to the sunlight filtering down from above. This is called counter illumination. Others use bioluminescence to distract or blind a predator whilst some animals use light as a lure to attract their prey. The anglerfish uses a light organ at the end of a "fishing rod" that extends from its head in order to tempt prey to within easy reach. Finding a mate in the endless darkness can be difficult, especially since deep sea animals tend to be solitary and widely distributed. Therefore bioluminescence can be used in courtship and mate selection, which makes it easier for some species to locate partners of their own kind.

Salt Lake In The Deep

Historically, the Gulf of Mexico was a shallow sea that became isolated from the ocean. As it dried out, thick layers of salts were produced. The basin then deepened and the connection with the ocean was re-established. The salt layers were protected from dissolving into the water column by a covering of sediment. Over the years, the sediment layer became increasingly thicker and therefore heavier, causing the salt to deform and move. In some areas, the salt layer has erupted through the sediment. When salt deposits come into contact with seawater, they dissolve and form brines, many times saltier than seawater and therefore heavier. Throughout the Gulf of

Warm Abyssal Plains

Just as one gets used to the rules, an exception occurs, and this is true even for the deep sea.

Mexico, warm salty fluids have pushed up-wards through cracks in the sediments and have formed puddles, pools and lakes of brine with distinct surfaces and shorelines. One of the most studied of these features is named the "Brine Pool" and is a rich source of met-hane which acts as an energy supply for bac-teria that supports dense colonies of mussels. The water in the lake is so dense that any ani-mal that falls into it dies instantly - even the submersibles that investigate these habitats are not able to penetrate the surface!

At over 600 m deep, a large community of mussels rings a pool of brine on the seafloor in the Gulf of Mexico.
© Charles Fisher, Penn State University

"Normal" abyssal plains are very cold because water is heaviest at temperatures just above freezing (ice, however, is lighter so that even huge icebergs swim), so the coldest water eventually sinks to the bottom. In the Mediterranean Sea, however, which is linked to the Atlantic Ocean through the narrow Straits of Gibraltar, relatively little water flows in to make up for the loss through evaporation caused by the warm sun. Consequently, the surface water becomes salter, just like in a salt pan, and becomes heavier and heavier until it sinks to the bottom. The water column therefore has nearly the same temperature from surface to bottom, something known much better from cold Polar waters. The big difference is that near the poles, very little organic matter is consumed in the water so that much of it can be eaten on the seafloor. In the warm waters of the Mediterranean, almost all of the organic matter is eaten before it ever has a chance to get to the seafloor, which results in the Mediterranean being one of the most nutrient depleted deep sea regions on Earth. As a consequence, it is possible that the distribution of bottom-dwelling animals in the Mediterranean is not influenced by depth, but rather by distance from land. As so little rains down from the surface, nutrients coming from the dry land via rivers or storms may be an important alternative food source.

Larvae Go Home!

The life-cycle of a giant vent tubeworm (Riftia pachyptila) is a treacherous and yet rather

spectacular one! This worm releases its eggs and sperm into the surrounding waters, fertilisation occurs and larvae are formed. For years, scientists have puzzled over how these larvae manage to get from one place to another and how they manage to survive the sometimes lengthy journey in such cold, dark conditions. Catastrophic volcanic eruptions can wipe out entire hydrothermal vent communities in just a few minutes! Therefore the ability to colonise new vent sites tens to hundreds of kilometres away is essential to the survival of the species.

Scientists decided they needed to collect some of the tubeworm larvae and see how long they could survive by simulating vent conditions in the laboratory. The little larvae survived for up to 38 days without food (they have internal stores of food) – time enough for them to find a new home many kilometres away. They may hitch a ride within hot vent waters that mix with the cold seawater, forming buoyant plumes. Water currents then transport the larvae on a kind of motorway in the sea, dropping them off at their final destination. For those that survive this perilous journey, they know when they have arrived at a decent spot – they can probably detect the toxic sulphide in the water or sense the elevated heat – a paradise for tubeworms is found!

A watercolour of the dragonfish, *Neonesthes capensis*, by Thorolv Rasmussen from 1910 – The Michael Sars expedition. © Bergen Museum

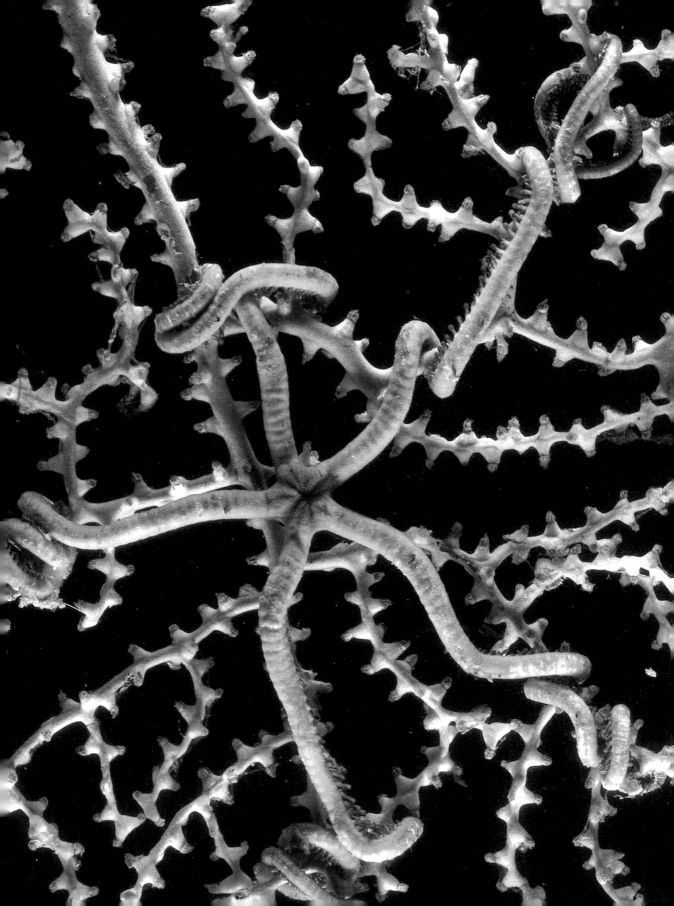

An Extension Of The Human Senses

In 2004 an international team of scientists undertook an expedition to the Mid-Atlantic Ridge to uncover some of the mysteries of the deep. The following account is a day in the life of a scientist on board:

25 Hours On A Super Station

"The alarm clock goes an hour before the ship arrives on station. I dare not look at the time; all I know is that it is way too early for me to be up and working! We have 13 super stations, which we plan to sample and this station today is located at 3500 m water depth. A total of 25 hours is required in order for us to complete all our work which consists of trawling at different depths, collecting water and plankton samples and undertaking hydrographic operations to name but a few. Since the instruments we are using are technologically sophisticated, many of the tasks we have to do can be conducted simultaneously.

Firstly let me tell you about the ship. The Norwegian research vessel, the *G. O. Sars*, is a relatively new state-of-the- art research vessel. Like some other new vessels, it has vibration-

A brittle star clings tightly
to a gorgonian coral.
© David Shale

and noise- damped diesel generators and propellers, which emit 99 % less noise than other conventional research vessels. This is a great advantage when scientists are doing acoustic monitoring of fish and animals in the sea and bliss when you are desperate for some sleep after a long hard shift.

The plan of work at each station is the same. The shift starts with the deployment of the ROBIO **Lander**. This a baited time-lapse camera attached to a tripod that free falls through the water column. Once on the seafloor it takes pictures of animals attracted to the bait but we have to wait until the system comes on to the ship before we can finally see what was there. As the Lander falls to the seabed, we then use a **CTD**-rosette to collect water samples from just below the surface to a few metres off the seafloor. Analysis of the temperature and salinity of the water at different depths gives us an idea of the type of environment that the animals inhabit. On the

CTD rosette, a video camera mounted above a screen records bioluminescent organisms hitting the screen as the rosette descends through the water column. The frequency of flashes of light given off by different animals in the water column can be used to study abundance of light-producing organisms in different layers.

One of the major tasks is to trawl through the water column and on the seafloor. However, before we can do this we need to make a map of the seafloor; the existing ones are not detailed enough for us to trawl without damaging the nets. To map an area of 5 x 5 km, the ship steams back and forth over the area with the **multi-beam echosounder** switched on which allows us to "see" and "hear" what the seafloor looks like. Once the fisheries biologists are happy that they are not going to destroy their nets, the trawl is lowered into the water. The trawls used are enormous; the mouth of the trawl varies from a few centimetres to 85 m and the largest mid-water trawl used aboard the *G.O. Sars* is large enough to have fished up the Eiffel Tower!! Trawling takes a long time (about 4 hours), what with paying out 5000 m of wire, even though we are only in 3500 m of water, the trawling on the bottom and then the hauling in of a net that now weighs considerably more than when it was deployed. The trawl also has a camera attached to allow us to see what fishes, cephalopods and other animals enter the trawl.

For many years sampling in rocky areas has proved problematic to scientists. But with recent technological developments, such as

The *Nautile*, launched in 1984, is one of the few manned submersibles that can descend to 6000 m water depth. It is capable of exploring 97 % of the world's ocean floors. © Ifremer/Eric Lacoupelle

Right: A boxcorer, having been recovered from the abyssal seafloor is moved ready for researchers to investigate what inhabits this part of the deep sea. © Armin Rose

ROV's (Remotely Operated Vehicles) and Landers, we are able to view and sample the deep sea in ways that scientists of the past could never have imagined. Twenty-four hours after we arrived on station we have reached the end of our sampling programme, it is now time for me to head to my cabin, briefly make some notes on what has happened today, plan what is happening tomorrow and then head for my bunk."

The Remotely Operated Vehicle (ROV) *Isis* with the ability to explore the seabed down to 6500 m. © National Oceanography Centre, Southampton

Norwegian Research Vessel *G.O. Sars*, used for the 2004 MAR-ECO expedition to the Mid-Atlantic Ridge. © David Shale

Use Your Senses To Sample The Deep Sea

Deep sea biological exploration only began about 170 years ago. The fascinating creatures brought back by naturalists from the first pioneering expeditions stimulated the development of a host of new technology required to gain a glimpse of this remote habitat in which we cannot walk around to touch, see, hear or smell. So, as an extension of our senses, we use novel technology to explore the deep sea.

See – Submersible

There is nothing like "seeing for yourself" to understand life on the ocean floor, which can be achieved with a submersible or its unmanned cousin, a robot called ROV. Submersibles are about as big as a large car, with usually two scientists and one pilot sharing a 2 m sphere (a hollow body of any other shape would be crushed by the pressure). Energy for cameras, lights and propellers comes from batteries, limiting the time on the bottom to a precious few hours. However, the ROV is steered and powered from the ship and thus can be a lot smaller. Video and stills cameras are the scientist's eyes looking around whilst on the bottom, for potentially 24 hours a day. Sometimes the air in the crowded pilots' lab is so thick with excitement and suspense you can cut it with a knife!

Touch – Trawling And Coring

Stretching out your hand to pick up an object of interest is one of the most basic human reactions. How often you have heard or spoken the words "look but don't touch"?! To touch something from the deep sea floor, we have to extend our hands down through 5000 m of water.

For about 100 years this was achieved by either towing a net behind the ship or by cutting out a piece of the seafloor. Towed gear can be shaped in many different ways, depending on the reason for the sample being collected, not least the size of animals researchers hope to catch. Nets with a solid metal frame at their opening are called dredges, and a metal frame keeping the net or nets at a defined distance from the seafloor (about 0.5 to 1 m) is called an epibenthic sled. Grabs and corers also come in different shapes and sizes, mostly developed to deliver samples of a defined area with undisturbed surfaces, which includes collecting a few centimetres of the overlying water. The animals have to be separated from the sediment by using a sieve, a delicate and often time consuming task.

The greatest living space on Earth is the mid-water realm. Sampling this 3D space is a great challenge, and mid-water samplers of

Another interesting camera system is the Sediment Profile Imaging System (SPI camera). It can look though the top 20 cm of sediment; imagine slicing through a block of cheese. It is a way of seeing how animals living in the sediment interact with their environment. For example how burrowing worms change the oxygen concentration by their aerating activities. With a little bit of luck, the animals themselves are caught on camera.

The new British Research Vessel, James Cook.
© National Oceanography Centre, Southampton

The French Research Vessel Pourquoi Pas?
© Ifremer/Olivier Dugornay

The orange roughy, Hoplostethus atlanticus, is thought to be able to live for 150 years. This is an impressive specimen, probably close to the species' maximum size. © Thomas de Lange Wenneck

various designs have been constructed to sample everything from the minute to the huge. The variability in the fauna related to depth is very pronounced, hence using gears that can sample discrete depth zones in a single operation is important. Large mid-water fish trawls can now capture animals from different depths in separate containers in just one operation. Multi-net zooplankton samplers of various designs have become very efficient, and the tiniest animals, algae and other particles can be recorded with profiling video camera systems.

Hear — Acoustics

Using reflected sound pulses, scientists are not only able to "see" underwater but also can "hear" underwater using sonar, a technique used by many marine animals. The echosounders that are used by scientists are really an extension of our ears. They are devices that emit sound and listen to the echo from the water or seafloor. An echosounder lets you "hear" the depth of the sea-floor (bathymetry) and also allows you to "hear" what the seabed is made of. For example soft mud may be differentiated from sand or rocky ground. Special echosounders let you "hear" under the sediment surface, and tell us something about the history of the seafloor. Sound can also be reflected off organisms found in the water column, a technique used in shallow water for many years to detect and identify fish.

Such techniques have greatly improved in recent years and modern echosounders operated from silent ships can detect organisms to about 3000 m. Echosounders mounted on landers on the seabed look (or listen) upwards and can be used to study movements of fish and plankton in the entire water column.

Smell — AUVs

"Smelling" under water seems hard to imagine, but smell is

The cod-end aquarium being retrieved. The aquarium helps keep specimens in good condition. It also has an internal digital video camera. © MAR-ECO

really nothing but a chemical sense, just detecting molecules. In the deep sea our noses are sensors mounted on a robot that can swim by itself on a pre-programmed route. These robots, which can operate in water as deep as 6000 m and cover large areas, are called Autonomous Underwater Vehicles (AUVs).

Most sensors work electrically or electronically, measuring changes in electrical conductivity caused by a certain chemical such as oxygen. They basically consist of a glass probe that is held into the water to pick up the chemical it is built to "smell" and an instrument that makes the result visible to the human eye, usually as some kind of a deflection along a scale or graphically as a curve. Data are stored on board the AUV and transferred directly to a computer on the ship. Scientists may then use these data in conjunction with other oceanographic data to build a picture of ocean processes.

Deck-view of the RV G.O. Sars equipped ready for an expedition. © MAR-ECO

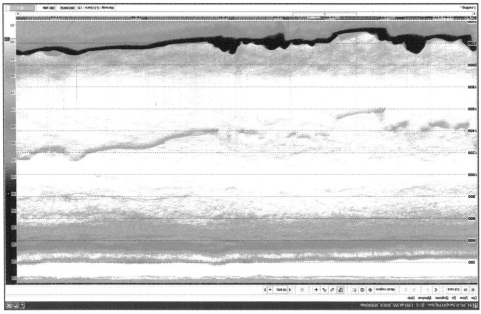

Perspectives

The last 170 years of scientific discovery have brought about revolutionary changes in the way in which we understand the deep seas and open ocean.

These advances in marine science have been brought about by new technologies for sensing and measurement, new vehicles and navigation systems enabling work in remote and difficult areas, and the use of computers to synthesize and analyse vast amounts of data. Collectively, the collaborations of scientists and explorers of the physical, chemical and biological qualities of the deep oceans are providing a new framework for understanding the interdependence of the physical and biological realms, and issues of human influence on the environment as a whole.

We now know that the deep ocean basins are relatively recent formations of the Earth's crust, made through the slow separation of the main continental land masses. And, although the first steps in the evolution of biological life took place in primitive seas, the present fauna of the deep ocean is based mostly on invasions of these basins by animal types already living closer to the surface. Key to the success of this colonisation is the supply of oxygen-rich, cold and salty water circulating into the deep ocean basins from the surface at the Polar Regions. This global ocean current system, driven by the cooling of surface water at the poles, is essential to maintaining life in the depths of the ocean. It underlies the discovery that the ocean basins are not some isolated and archaic world but a dynamic zone of the

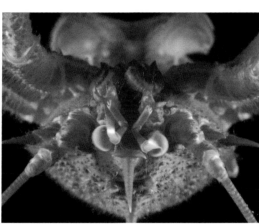

A galatheid crab, *Munidopsis* sp. © David Shale

Left, top: Echo sounder image showing layers of organisms form the surface to 2100 m depth, seen via sound scattering. © Ruben Patel

Left, bottom: The Autonomous Underwater Vehicle ABE (Autonomous Benthic Explorer) was the first underwater robot vehicle of its kind and can manoeuvre independently in three dimensions. © Chris German, Woods Hole Oceanographic Institution

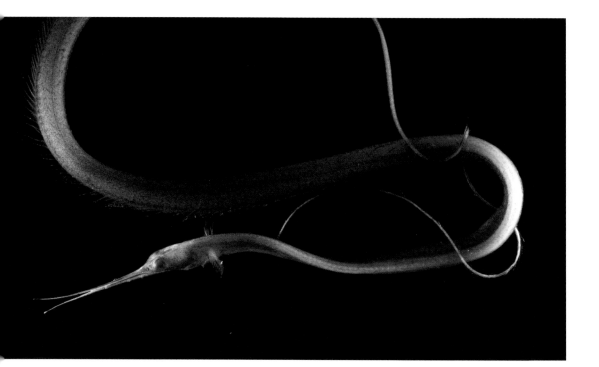

© David Shale

A snipe eel, *Nemichthys* sp., an extremely elongate midwater fish with a pair of very peculiar long, thin set jaws.

Conditions of life

Key conditions in the deep ocean setting the boundaries of biological life have given rise to some of the most distinctive adaptive features of the marine animals. Notable are the lack of natural light, the effects of pressure from the depth of the water, and the low productivity of the environment.

Light production by deep living creatures is one of their most distinctive features and is involved in many fundamental aspects of their lives such as finding food, avoiding predators, or reproduction. It occurs within practically all groups of animals adapted to the dark environment and arises from a wide diversity of specialized structures and biochemical specialisms, often involving symbiotic relationships with micro-organisms.

The need for neutral buoyancy and energy conservation in the high pressure environment of the deep sea has led to the specialised biological adaptation of various structures. Animals of many sorts have made use of various biochemical and physical properties to lighten

global ocean, potentially responsive to any changes in the global climate system affecting ocean circulation.

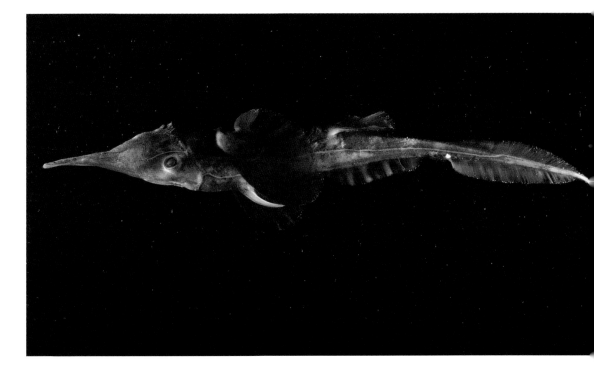

A chimaera, *Harriotta haeckeli*, also known as the rabbitfish, is one of the deepest-living species of elasmobranch fishes.

© David Shale

heavy skeletal tissues and to accumulate buoyant material in specialized ways allowing them to conserve energy while maintaining their position in space. Some of the most impressive adaptations in the deep sea can be seen in animals that inhabit the chemosynthetic environments of hydrothermal vents. Here, some animals have to cope not only with the dark and pressure, but also with massive changes in temperature. Many have also learned to thrive on the numerous chemoautotrophic bacteria by developing symbiotic relationships.

These highly specialized adaptations offer unique new sources of understanding and of genetic material of great potential value to science and medicine.

Vulnerability To The Human Impact

Current deep-sea research is making major contributions to the connectivity between the deep-sea environment and the world above. Although connectivity is intrinsic to the structure of the oceans and the continuity of water masses and biological life, it also means that the deep ocean is vulnerable to our present capacity to perturb conditions on a global scale.

The deep-sea world is on the verge of new scientific discovery daily, but already we can foresee many ways in which it can be affected by human activities either directly by targeted exploitation or indirectly through our impacts elsewhere in the global environment.

Evidence is already clear that uncontrolled extension of commercial fisheries targeted on deepwater resources can quickly damage their slow growing populations, and may inflict harmful effects on other by-catch species. The

release of long-lived chemical contaminants such as radionuclides and organohalides anywhere in the sea is shown to spread within decades to almost any part of the ocean. And the results of careless dumping and discarding of human rubbish is ever present.

In the future, we can expect greatly increased pressure for exploitation of both mineral and biological resources. But perhaps the greatest threats to the health of the oceans come from the possible impact of changes in

Watercolour by Ørnulf Opdahl. Impressions from the MAR-ECO expedition - 2004.

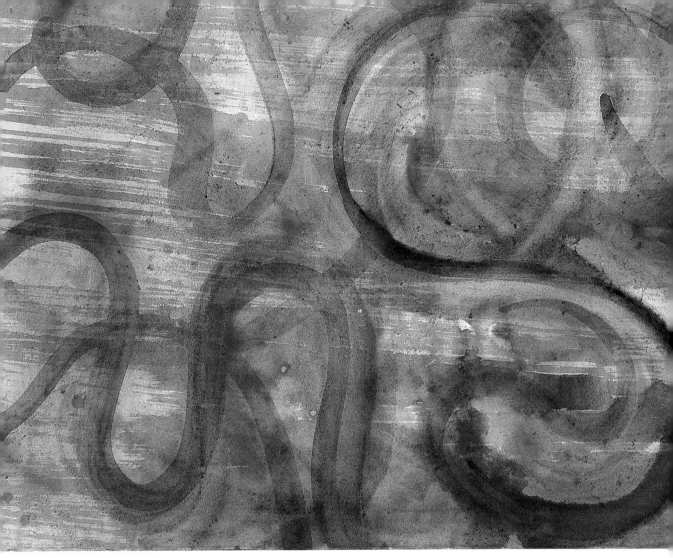

Below: Watercolour by Ørnulf Opdahl. Impressions from the MAR-ECO expedition - 2004.
Page 78-79: An explosion of colour in the deep sea: the hydrothermal vent tubeworm *Ridgeia piscesae*,
showing their beautiful red plumes. © Ian MacDonald, Texas A&M

biological production at the sea surface and shifts in the pattern of current flow and water transport on which life in the great oceans depends.

So much of the recognised harmful human impact on the terrestrial environment occurred before Man was arguably conscious of his capability to affect the Earth and its systems so profoundly. Our new scientific knowledge,

revealing the interdependence of the deep sea with the familiar world in which we live, must be brought urgently into commercial thinking and government policies concerning development of the oceans if we are to continue to make progress without unintended and potentially disastrous consequences.

Glossary

Abyssal Plains - vast expanses of flat seafloor covered by a thick layer of fine sediment. They are found between 3000 and 6000 m depth and cover approximately 40 % of the ocean floor.

Algae - relatively simple organisms that occur in most habitats. Through a process called photosynthesis, they convert inorganic substances into organic matter.

AUV - Autonomous Underwater Vehicle; a robot that is powered by batteries or sometimes fuel cells. They can operate in depths of up to 6000 m.

Azoic zone - a concept put forward by Edward Forbes where it was suggested that life would not exist below a depth of 600 m after undertaking dredging work at these depths in the Aegean sea.

Bathymetry - the study of underwater depth.

Benthic organisms or Benthos - organisms attached to, living on, or in the seabed.

Bioluminescence - is both the production and emission of light by a living organism. It is the result of a chemical reaction whereby chemical energy is converted to light energy.

Biosphere - part of the earth and its atmosphere in which living organisms exist or that is capable of supporting life.

Black Smoker - a type of hydrothermal vent found on the seabed. When superheated water in the vent comes in to contact with the cold seawater, many minerals are precipitated, creating the distinctive black colour.

Branchia - a synonym of gill. A respiratory organ of aquatic animals that breathe oxygen dissolved in water.

Carbonate Mounds - accumulation of dead coral skeletons, which over time form a mound on the seabed.

Chemosynthesis - the use of chemicals as an energy source as oppose to light (photosynthesis) to produce organic matter.

Cold Seeps - cold water laden with hydrogen sulphide, methane and other hydrocarbons, seeps onto the ocean floor. Cold seeps support chemosynthetic faunal communities alongside many non-chemosynthetic communities.

Continental Margin - a zone separating the emergent continents from the deep sea bottom, generally consisting of the continental shelf, slope and rise.

Continental Rise - area below the continental slope but before the abyssal plains are reached. The gradient of the continental rise is between 0.5 - 1°.

Continental Shelf - is characteristically of low inclination on the continental margin and extends from the coast to the shelf break, where the inclination increases and the continental slope begins (from 0 – 200 m depth).

Continental Slope - is characterised by steep inclination of the seabed (average 3°) and extends from the shelf break to the abyssal plain (from 200 – 3000 m).

Crustacean - group of animals belonging to the phylum *Arthropoda* containing many well known animals including crabs, shrimp and barnacles.

CTD - an oceanographic instrument that measures conductivity, temperature and depth.

Cytoplasm - is the semi-transparent, gelatinous like fluid which fills most cells.

Diurnal migration - the movement of animals through the water column on a daily basis.

Diversity - the number of species found in a specific habitat or community.

Echinoderm - a phylum of marine animals comprising of some well known groups such as sea stars and sea urchins, which are found at all depths of the world's oceans.

Ecosystem - this term refers to any collection of living and non-living components and processes that interact with each other.

Endemic - organisms that are only found in a specific area.

Foraminifera - these are a group of amoeboid fauna that generally produce a shell. They can have one or multiple chambers and are usually less than 1 mm in size.

Gelatinous - has a jelly like texture.

Glacial era or ice ages - intervals of time in the Earth's history when large areas are covered with ice sheets. Strictly speaking, because ice is found at the poles, the Earth experiences an ice age that has lasted for 30 million years. The last glacial maximum occurred 18 000 years ago when northern Europe and America were covered by the polar ice sheet.

Haemoglobin - is the iron-containing protein attached to red blood cells that transports oxygen around the body. The iron contained in haemoglobin gives the blood its red colour.

Hydrography - is the measurement and description of water.

Hydrothermal Fluid - is hot water laden with chemicals and metals emitted from hydrothermal vents.

Hydrothermal Vent - occur at fissures in the oceanic crust at mid-ocean ridges where geothermal super-heated fluid is expelled from the Earth's interior.

Komokiacea - similar to foraminifera. They have multiple openings, but lack true chambers.

Lander - autonomous lander vehicles are completely independent of the ship, and can be left to work on the seabed while the ship continues with other tasks.

Macrofauna - animals that are large enough to be seen with the naked eye. In the deep sea, fauna that are collected on a 0.25 mm sieve are also known as macrofauna.

Magma - molten rock found beneath the surface of the earth.

Marine snow - the basis of most deep sea food chains made of remains of plants and animals that drift down from the sunlit surface waters of the ocean to the depths.

Megafauna - animals that are large enough to be seen on photographs.

Mid-ocean ridges - volcanic mountain chain formed where two tectonic plates are being pulled apart and new seafloor is being formed.

Multi-beam echosounder - this is an instrument that is used to determine the distance of an object based on the time it takes for sound waves to travel to the object and back.

Nematode - also commonly known as roundworms. Extremely common in all environments and often outnumber other animals.

Nucleus - a membrane-enclosed organelle found within a cell, containing most of its genetic material.

Non-symbiotic corals - Corals that do not live in symbiosis with algae and have to sustain themselves by feeding on particles or live prey.

Ocean crust - part of the solid outermost shell (lithosphere) on Earth found in the ocean basins.

Pelagic - the part of the ocean or sea that is not near the sea floor or coast.

Plankton - plants and animals that inhabit, and drift, in the water column.

Photosynthesis - is the process undertaken by plants to convert water and carbon dioxide into sugars and carbohydrates using energy from the sun.

Phylum - a primary division of the animal kingdom e.g. Mollusca (squid, octopus, mussels) constitute a phylum.

Phytoplankton - plant like organisms of the sea that drift in the water column.

Productivity - the rate of production in an ecosystem.

Protists - a diverse group of organisms that cannot be classified in any another kingdom.

Pyrosome, a common name is corn cob jelly. Pyrosomes are not really jellyfish but instead belong to the phylum *Chordata*, animals with a backbone. The pyrosomes are hollow cylinders composed of thousands of individuals joined together in a gelatinous matrix.

Radiation - is energy transmitted in the form of waves, rays or particles.

Reversing thermometer - able to record the temperature at a given time and retain it until viewed later. When the thermometer is turned upside down the temperature reading will be preserved until the thermometer is turned the right way up.

ROV - Remotely Operated Vehicle; this is a tethered underwater robot operated from a research vessel.

Seamount - a mountain that rises from the ocean floor but does not reach the surface.

Spicule - form the skeleton of most sponges.

Stony coral - Scleractinia: are similar to sea anemones but produce a hard skeleton.

Submersible - an underwater, untethered vehicle which has limited mobility and is transported from one operational area to another by a ship or submarine.

Substrate - the surface on which an animal or plant may be attached.

Symbiosis - relationship between two different species with beneficial or deleterious consequences.

Taxonomy - is a scientific means of classifying organisms in an ordered system.

Tectonic Plates - seven large and many small rigid plates that form the Earth's crust and move in relation to one another.

Trophic - the position that an animal occupies in a food chain.

Trophosome - sac-like structure found in the bodies of hydrothermal vent and cold seep tubeworms filled with chemosynthetic bacteria.

Turbidity flow - A flow of dense, muddy water moving down the slope in strong underwater currents, which are usually triggered by earthquakes or slumping.

Whale fall - body of a dead whale sinking and transporting nutrients to the sea floor that may develop a chemosynthetic ecosystem.

Zooplankton - an animal which drifts within the water column of the oceans.

Acknowledgments

The Deep Sea Education and Outreach group (DESEO) would like to thank Fondation Total for the support provided in order to produce this book. We would also like to thank the European Census of Marine Life for funding the initial workshop where DESEO was formed and for their continued support.

We are very appreciative of all the people who have kindly agreed to let us use their photographs and drawings freely throughout the book; in particular we would like to thank Ørnulf Opdahl and David Shale.

We would also like to thank our colleagues who are individually working on the different deep-water Census of Marine Life projects, without whom this book would not be possible.

A sea anemone of the family *Hormathiidae* fixed on a colony of "black corals" *(Antipatharia)*.
© Ifremer/Caracole cruise 2001

REALLY REALLY BIG QUESTIONS
about Faith

 **KINGFISHER**

First published 2011 by Kingfisher
an imprint of Macmillan Children's Books
a division of Macmillan Publishers Limited
20 New Wharf Road, London N1 9RR
Basingstoke and Oxford
Associated companies throughout the world
www.panmacmillan.com

ISBN 978-0-7534-3151-1

Copyright © Macmillan Publishers Ltd 2011
Text © Julian Baggini 2011
Illustrations © Nishant Choksi 2011
www.nishantchoksi.com

1 3 5 7 9 8 6 4 2
1TR/0511/WKT/UNTD/140WF

A CIP catalogue record for this book is available from the British Library.

Printed in China

Note to readers: the website addresses listed in this book are correct at the time of going
to print. However, due to the ever-changing nature of the internet, website addresses
and content can change. Websites can contain links that are unsuitable for children.
The publisher cannot be held responsible for changes in website addresses or
content, or for information obtained through a third party. We strongly
advise that internet searches should be supervised by an adult.

REALLY REALLY BIG QUESTIONS

about Faith

Dr Julian Baggini

Illustrated by

Nishant Choksi

CONTENTS

CHAPTER 1
A RAINBOW OF RELIGIONS

CHAPTER 2
SEARCHING FOR GOD

CHAPTER 3
SAINTS, SINNERS, GOOD AND EVIL

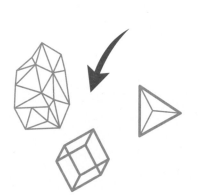

CHAPTER 4
LIVING WITH FAITH, GOD, SOULS AND ANGELS

WHAT ON EARTH

SHOULD WE BELIEVE?

DR JULIAN BAGGINI

Imagine you are a visitor to Earth from outer space. You would find a world of astonishing variety. From the window of your flying saucer, you would see vast seas of ice and snow, enormous mountain ranges, fields, forests and huge, flat deserts. You would see people living in tiny villages and in cities of millions.

But almost everywhere you went in the world, you would find signs of the same thing: *religion*. You would see a religious building – a church, a mosque, a synagogue, a temple – in almost every village, town or city. You would see people praying to or worshipping their gods, some regularly, some only from time to time. You would see religious symbols, such as crosses, in people's houses or worn around their necks.

"Religion is clearly very important to these Earthlings," you might think.

But what is this thing called 'religion'? Although it is everywhere, *why is it so different in different places?* Why do so many people believe it, and why do some reject it? What does each religion mean to its followers? Would the world be the same *without* religion?

Until you have answered questions like these, you wouldn't really understand Earthlings and how they live. And that's also true if you are an Earthling yourself, which I very much hope you are! To understand the world we live in, we need to understand the religions that fill it. And to do that, we're going to have to ask some really, really big questions...

1
A
RAINBOW
OF RELIGIONS

All over the world, throughout history, there are religions. Each one is different. For example, in Christianity, Islam and Judaism, there is only one God, but in Hinduism, there seem to be many. In Buddhism, there are no gods at all.

Why is there so much variety? Which religion, if any, should we believe? And how should we deal with the fact that people disagree about the really important things religions tell us?

WHAT is RELIGION?

Religions have three things in common.

First, they involve a set of beliefs about how the world was created, why we are here and how we should live. In almost every religion, some of these beliefs are *supernatural*. This doesn't mean that religious people believe in ghosts or witches. All it means is that the religious believe there is more to our world than what we see around us in nature. There is also God, gods, souls or spirits.

Second, religions almost always involve certain *activities*. Believers do things like pray, worship, meditate, read holy books and give money to the poor. Religion is not only about what you *think*, it's also about what you *do*.

Third, religions are usually communities of some kind. To belong to a religion is to belong to a group of people who will meet up and help each other.

HOW DO WE UNDERSTAND RELIGION?

People who have different beliefs to our own can seem weird! A Christian, for example, might think it funny that one of the Hindu gods, Ganesha, has the head of an elephant. But a Hindu might find it even more bizarre that a common Christian ceremony, the communion, apparently involves eating the body and blood of Jesus.

Accepting that our beliefs can appear just as strange as other people's may help us to realize that *we are not that different after all*.

So how do we *understand* religion? We can look at what their special books tell us. We can read the Bible to understand Christianity, the Koran to understand Islam, or the Bhagavad Gita to understand Hinduism.

We can also listen to what *religious leaders* say. Rabbis teach their communities about Judaism, while imams are Muslim leaders. The Pope is an authority on what Roman Catholicism means today, while the Dalai Lama speaks for Tibetan Buddhism.

Books and leaders do not tell us *everything,* however. People disagree about the meaning of the stories in religious books, and religious leaders can disagree among themselves.

So we can't just ask people for the answers to the really big questions we have about religion, and we can't just look them up – even in this book! *We have to think for ourselves*.

WHY ARE THERE SO MANY RELIGIONS?

There are *so many different religions* in the world that counting them isn't easy. Even if you stick to the biggest ones, there are more than 20 with more than half a million followers each.

So why is there all this variety?

One possibility is that only one, or some, of the world's religions are true, and that the rest are mistakes. One problem with that answer is, *how do we know which one is right?*

Another possibility is that every religion is wrong in some way, but many – perhaps all – have got *some* things right.

A third possibility is that religions are all just *human inventions*. Of course, people don't think they are just making it up. Religious people genuinely believe they have discovered truths and not just invented stories. But maybe they are wrong.

Which is the right answer? I can't tell you that. You have to decide for yourself which one makes more sense.

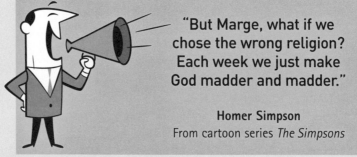

"But Marge, what if we chose the wrong religion? Each week we just make God madder and madder."

Homer Simpson
From cartoon series *The Simpsons*

WHY ARE THERE DIFFERENT
KINDS OF THE SAME RELIGION?

There are so many different religions that if you were to buy them from a shop, it would have to be a huge supermarket. And just as supermarkets sell different varieties of the same thing – pasta, chocolate bars, washing powders – many of the world's religions offer different varieties too.

For example, among the world's two billion Christians, you'll find Anglicans, Methodists, Roman Catholics, Eastern Orthodox, Baptists, Evangelicals... the list could go on and on.

The reason for this is that over time, *a religion often splits into different groups*. These groups may then undergo their own divisions, and so on. You can see how easily religions multiply!

But *why* does a religion split in the first place? Usually it's because its members disagree – either about what the teachings of the religion should be or who has the right to hold power within it.

Because religious people are human, they get caught up in the same kind of rivalries and power games that other human beings do too.

So in a way there's no mystery about why religions split: *religious people disagree because all people disagree, religious or not!*

SHOULD WE RESPECT PEOPLE FROM DIFFERENT RELIGIONS?

In some parts of the world, at some times in history, people were expected to follow one religion and *one religion only*. Those who refused were either thrown out of their country, imprisoned or killed.

Nowadays, the United Nations recognizes the freedom to practise the religion of our choice as a basic human right.

We respect people with different beliefs because we know that religion matters very much to people, and even if we think they are wrong, we cannot be sure that we are right. Respect involves accepting that *no one knows for sure what the truth about God and religion is*.

However, that does not mean that we must respect *anything* that people do, even if they say they do it because of their religion. We do not respect people who kill others in the name of their religion, or who persecute those who disagree with them. We respect people's right to believe as long as they behave in a good and decent way. That sounds fair, doesn't it?

WHY ARE SOME COUNTRIES MORE RELIGIOUS THAN OTHERS?

A few years ago, a survey discovered that nine out of ten people in Africa said they were religious. In Latin America and the Middle East, eight out of ten people said they were. But in western Europe, only six out of ten people said they were religious.

So why are some parts of the world more religious than others? Well, it often seems that richer countries with more education are less religious.

But it is not as simple as that. The United States is a very religious country, with more than seven out of every ten people describing themselves as religious. But it is also the richest country in the world, with high levels of education. All over the world, there are people who are rich, educated *and* religious.

So although wealth and education do play a role, we must look at the *history and culture of each individual country* to see why people there believe what they do. There are so many factors involved that it's hard to work out why some countries are more religious than others!

CAN WE CRITICIZE RELIGION?

Some people get very angry when other people criticize their religion. And some people have even been killed because they criticized another person's religion.

But criticism can be a *good thing* – although it depends what you *mean* by criticism. It doesn't just mean to say bad things about something; criticism also means to debate, to analyze, to discuss something fully and give your opinion. Unless you think that all religions are perfect, you must think that this sort of criticism should be allowed.

So remember, what's important is *how* you criticize. The best criticism is not rude, but polite and helpful – the way your teacher might comment on your homework or a sports coach might assess his or her players.

But make sure you know your facts first – *you can't discuss someone else's religion if you don't know enough about it!*

WAS THERE REALLY A GREAT FLOOD?

The Christian Bible, the Jewish Torah and the Muslim Koran all contain remarkable stories of miracles and strange events.

One of the most famous is the Great Flood. In the version shared by Jews and Christians, God says to a good man called Noah,

"I am going to bring floodwaters on the Earth to destroy all life under the heavens, every creature that has the breath of life in it."

He tells Noah to build a big boat, an ark, to save his family and "two of all living creatures, male and female". The floods come, and the Ark saves Noah, his family and all the animals. Life on Earth continues.

But could this *really* have happened?

How could Noah have found room for two of *every single type of animal,* even in a huge boat? How could there ever have been enough rain to flood *the entire world*? And how would he have got hold of *penguins* in his Middle Eastern home? Perhaps you can think of other reasons why the flood was unlikely.

Most people don't think the Great Flood really happened. The same is true of other incredible stories, like the one about Jonah, who was swallowed by a whale and lived to tell the tale. Most people think they are *stories*, not *historical facts*. But such stories can be important too. They can teach believers about what God wants and how we should live.

Some people, however, do believe that all the stories in their holy books really did happen. What do *you* think?

2

SEARCHING FOR GOD

Who's in charge around here? I don't mean of your house, your school or your town – I mean of *the world, the Universe, the whole thing!* Maybe *nobody* is (which is why it rains on holiday and too much chocolate makes your teeth fall out).

But many religions say that the Universe does have *some kind of controller*. And for most people, that controller is an amazing being called 'God'. *God* made us, *God* looks after us, *God* will reward us if we do the right thing and punish us if we do wrong. And God can do *anything*. Sounds pretty amazing, eh? So where is this God then?

Let's go take a look for him.

Or is it a *her?*
Or an *it?*
Or even a *them?*

SURPRISE!

WHAT IS GOD?

Those who believe in God all agree that, whatever he is, he's far more amazing than any human being. Most people think he has *three super-powers*.

First, he's *all-knowing*. You can't hide anything from him. Organizing a surprise party for him would be a complete waste of time.

Second, he's *all-powerful*. He can do *anything*. Most religious people believe he created the entire Universe.

Third, he is *all-loving*. Some people think he is willing to punish the wicked, but all he really wants is the best for us, his creations.

All-knowing, all-powerful and all-loving – sounds like he's got it all!

"If God did not exist, it would be necessary to invent him."

Voltaire (1694–1778)
French philosopher

DOES GOD EXIST?

This God may sound incredible, but remember 'incredible' literally means 'unbelievable'. So is the idea of God hard to believe? Could such an amazing being really exist?

Non-religious people who don't believe God exists are known as *atheists*. There are also some people, such as Buddhists, who are religious but do not believe in God. And there are many *animist religions*, whose followers believe not in God but in spirits that are part of all living things.

Even when two people both say they *do* believe in God, it sometimes turns out that they have very different ideas about *who this God is*. So even when people agree that God does exist, they might disagree about *which* God exists!

COULD THERE BE MORE THAN ONE GOD?

Some religions have gods, but not the single, super-powerful God most are familiar with from Christianity, Judaism and Islam. Instead, they believe in *lots of gods*, ones that take care of different parts of the world or of life. In ancient Greek religion, for example, Aphrodite was the goddess of love and beauty and Poseidon was the god of the sea.

Many people know that Hinduism is a religion with thousands of gods. Some see these gods as forms in which the one true God, Brahman, shows himself to us. Some believe that Brahman is like a person who thinks about us and cares for us, whereas others believe that Brahman is more like a supreme force or energy.

Nowadays, the world's biggest religions believe in one God, and one God only. But the most popular view is not always the right one. Maybe there are many gods; maybe there are none.

CAN WE PROVE GOD EXISTS?

We can't scientifically observe God, like we can animals, objects or places, but nonetheless some people think they can prove he exists. That would be pretty impressive! However, most people think these 'proofs' don't work.

One such argument is that *everything must have a cause*. Even the cause of the Universe – the Big Bang – itself had a cause. But you can't keep going back to earlier causes forever. Eventually, you have to end up with *a first cause* – something that was powerful and amazing enough to create the Big Bang and the Universe, but that wasn't created by anything else. What could be that amazing? *God*, of course!

The problem is that if you state that *everything must have a cause*, you can't avoid the question, "What caused God?" But if you say that *nothing caused God*, then it's not true that everything must have a cause! So maybe the Universe doesn't need a cause and the existence of God is not necessary after all.

Another argument is that the Universe is so wonderfully well organized that *something must have designed it*. Think of the way the bees, the plants, the sun and the rain all fit so well together, so that life keeps growing thoughout the seasons.

The trouble is that science has helped explain – without the need for a god – how it is that different lifeforms depend on each other. It may look as though it's all beautifully 'designed', but there's no design at all – it's just *nature* taking its course.

There are other arguments, and people spend whole lifetimes arguing for or against them. But most serious thinkers about religion do not think that God's existence can be proved. There may be good reasons for or against believing in God, but there is no single proof that can settle the issue once and for all. That's why we're still disagreeing about it after many thousands of years of human existence!

WHAT DOES GOD LOOK LIKE?

Vatican City in Rome, Italy, is the home of the Roman Catholic Church, the world's biggest Christian group. If you go to the palace of the Pope, the church's leader, and into the Sistine Chapel, look up at the ceiling. You'll see one of the most famous paintings of God ever.

He is shown as an old but strong man, with white hair and a beard. He reaches out his finger to give life to Adam, the first human being.

When Christianity's God is pictured, it is usually something like this. Presenting him that way makes him seem wise, mature, kind and approachable.

It helps us to have an idea of God, but Michelangelo's painting on the ceiling of the chapel does not show us what he *really* looks like. What God really looks like is a *mystery*.

Some religious traditions, such as those of Judaism and Islam, do not allow their followers to make any images of God at all. God's appearance is completely unknown, they say, and it is sinful even to attempt to guess what it is.

Whether religions allow us to picture God or not, no one can really say what God looks like.

IS GOD A MAN?

Look at all those pictures of the Christian God and what you almost always see is an old *man*. Read religious texts and God is 'He' and often called 'Our Father'. So does that mean God is definitely a man?

If that's what the holy books say, some people believe, it must be true.

But there's something odd about that. You get males and females among animals and people because animals and people produce children. But God is not an animal – or even a person like you or me. And although Jesus is said to be the son of God, he is not God's child in a 'normal' father-and-son way.

So why is God usually thought of as being a man? *Do we need to think of God as having a gender at all?*

Although God is beyond our complete understanding, perhaps we have to talk about him (and paint him) in ways that fit what we think we do understand about him. We think of God as a man because that helps us to imagine him better.

But why a *man*? Why not a *woman*?

The answer is probably that for most of human history, men have had more power than women. Our image of the most powerful being in the Universe was created in the image of the most powerful people on Earth – men.

DID GOD CREATE THE WORLD?

Most people who believe in God think that he did one very important thing: he created the Universe, including our world and everything in it. Almost every religion has a story about how he did this. One Hindu story has the God of creation, Brahma, making the world from the leaves of a lotus flower. In the Christian and Jewish traditions, God created the heavens and Earth over six days and rested on the seventh.

Some people think these stories are completely true. Most, however, think they are just colourful ways of expressing the idea that God created the world in some way, perhaps in a way that we don't understand.

All these stories, however, came before modern science. We now know that the Universe began nearly 14 billion years ago with the Big Bang. Our sun and our planet, Earth, began to take shape just over four and a half billion years ago and human beings evolved about 200,000 years ago. Almost every scientist agrees that we do not need God to explain any of these developments.

CAN GOD DO ANYTHING?

God is usually thought to be all-powerful. But here are some things it seems he *can't* do:

God can't make another god who is even more powerful than himself.

God can't create a square circle. If it had four sides, it wouldn't be a circle; if it were a circle, it wouldn't have four sides and so it couldn't be square.

And God couldn't make a cake too big for God to eat! If he couldn't eat something, that would mean he couldn't do everything and he wouldn't be all-powerful.

In other words, even God can't do what is literally impossible. *Perhaps he cannot be all-powerful.*

BRAIN BURN!

If God is all good, does that mean he cannot choose to do evil?

DOES GOD KNOW MY FUTURE?

If God knows *everything*, does he know what you're going to do next?

Here's a scary thought. If God does know everything, then he knows what you're going to do at 09:43am in 20 years' time.

Does that mean *your future is fixed?*

Well, maybe God doesn't know the future. Maybe God knows only everything *it is possible to know* – and surely it is impossible to know the future.

Or maybe he *does* know the future. But that doesn't mean your choices won't change the future. Your future choices are all free, it's just that God can see ahead and know what they're going to be.

If God does know the future, however, it does raise a difficult question: *why would he allow children to be born if he knew they were going to grow into evil criminals, or live miserable lives?*

MUST WE OBEY GOD?

Most religions are very clear that God must be obeyed. Their holy books often contain stories that warn of what happens to those who don't. In the Bible, for example, God destroys the cities of Sodom, Gomorrah, Admah and Zeboim and everyone in them, because their people have not followed his laws.

But even if you think you must obey God, *how do you know what God wants?* Different people look to the same holy books and find different answers. It's hard to obey God if it's not clear what he wants!

Most religions say we should do God's will – meaning we should do what he wants us to do. But we should be careful when people tell us that they know what God wants. *How do they know?*

SHOULD WE FEAR GOD?

Some people describe themselves as 'God-fearing'. They think that this is a good thing. We are *supposed* to fear God. In the Bible, it says, "Fear God and keep his commandments, for this is the whole duty of man."

But *why* fear God? Well, imagine that you think that God is the most powerful thing in the whole Universe. He could send you to heaven or to live forever in hell. Or he could just end your life completely. He knows everything, so when he judges you, there is nowhere for you to hide the bad things you've done. That *is* a bit scary, isn't it?

But others say that because God is love, there is nothing to be afraid of. God will always do what's best for us, *because he wants what's best for us,* he knows what's best for us, and he can do anything he wants for us.

Nothing to be afraid of then?

WHAT IF THERE IS NO

GOD?

Some people believe that there is no God. They are called *atheists*.

Would it matter if God didn't exist? Many people think it would. If the Universe had no creator, and no good guy in charge, then how do we know *how* to live, *and what's the point of living in the first place?*

Most atheists disagree. They think life can be good with no God or gods. Indeed, isn't it better to treat others well just because you think you ought to, and not because you're trying to keep on God's good side? Isn't it better to appreciate life for what it is, rather than thinking too much about what might follow it?

Atheists say that living without God helps us to focus on what really matters: our fellow human beings and life here on Earth.

So if God does not exist, it may not be such a disaster after all!

"Religion is something left over from the infancy of our intelligence. It will fade away as we adopt reason and science as our guidelines."

Bertrand Russell (1872–1970)
British philosopher

3

SAINTS, SINNERS, GOOD AND EVIL

When people want to know what's right and what's wrong, they often turn to holy books or to religious leaders. And there are many rules religions agree about. Almost all tell us to look after the poor and not to murder or steal.

But other rules are very different. Muslims and Jews, for instance, are forbidden to eat pork, Hindus are not allowed to eat beef, and most Buddhists are vegetarian.

So, with all these different ideas floating about, *is religion the best and most reliable guide to how we should behave?*

GOD'S WHEEL OF RIGHT & WRONG!

DOES RELIGION DETERMINE WHAT'S
RIGHT AND WRONG?

More than two thousand years ago, a philosopher called Plato asked, "Is what is good loved by the gods because it is good, or is it good because it is loved by the gods?"

That's a complicated question! *What did he mean?* Well, think about all the things that we think are good, like being kind and honest. Religious people believe that God wants us to be kind and honest and good in other ways too. But *why* does God want that?

One possibility is that kindness and honesty are good things, *and God always wants what is good*.

The other possibility is that *things are good only because God wants them*. If God wanted you to be mean and dishonest, those things would be good, and their opposites, kindness and honesty, would have to be bad.

Which option do you think is true? Are things good only because God wants them or does God want them because they are good?

If you think that things are good only because God wants them, that's a bit strange. It means that everything good could be bad, and everything bad could be good.

Most people think that God wants good things because they are good. But that means *they're good anyway*, no matter what God wants. *God doesn't make them good or bad*.

So does this mean that we don't need God – or religion – to know that there is a difference between right and wrong? Or do you think that we need God to help *show us* what is good and bad?

WHAT IS A SIN?

A sin is something that a religion says is wrong. If you don't believe in God, then you don't believe in sin – but you might still believe that some things are right and some things are wrong. The difference between a sin and something that is just wrong is that *a sin breaks the law of God*.

Of course, it can be pretty scary to think you have disobeyed the most powerful thing in the Universe. If you think you have sinned, you might feel very guilty and afraid of God's punishment. Some atheists think that is why religions may have created the idea of sin – it frightens people into doing what their leaders want.

What do you think? *Is sin real* or *is it an idea that religions have invented?*

AM I BORN A SINNER?

Judaism, Islam and Christianity all tell the story of Adam and Eve, the first people God created. He allowed them to live in the Garden of Eden, which had everything they needed. *All they had to do was not eat the fruit that grew on the 'tree of knowledge and good and evil'.*

They blew it. Tempted by the devil, who took the shape of a snake, *they ate the fruit* and were thrown out of the garden. From that day on, some religious traditions say, every person is born guilty of the sin of Adam and Eve.

Most people don't think this story actually happened, but that it teaches a lesson: *human beings are not born perfect*. Maybe a baby hasn't yet done anything wrong, but *nobody* grows up completely innocent.

For many religious people, this means we all need God's forgiveness. For others, perhaps it is simply a reminder that we are a mixture of good and bad, and we should not think that we're better than we really are.

ARE RELIGIOUS PEOPLE BETTER?

Chang is a 'devout Taoist'. Gurpreet is a 'pious Sikh'. Aisha is a 'good Muslim'.

Why do we describe people like this? It's because we think that being a devoted member of a religion shows that you are a good, trustworthy person. Gurpreet is 'pious', meaning he follows his religion's teachings carefully. Chang is 'devout', meaning that he is also dedicated to following his religion. If that is true, then you would not expect Chang to be a bad person, who lies or steals (or has a nasty habit of ignoring the poor and needy on his way to the temple).

Does that mean that religious people are, in general, *better* than non-religious people? Not necessarily. When we say Aisha is a 'good Muslim', we are not only saying that she is good, we are also saying something about *why* and *how* she is good. For her, the Muslim way of life gives her reasons and guidance to be good. But that does not mean other people can't be good for other reasons.

It is also possible to be a *bad* Taoist, Sikh or Muslim, of course. Being religious does not automatically make you good.

So although having a religion to follow can help people to live good lives, you can be a good, non-religious person or a bad, religious one.

WHAT ARE SAINTS?

Many religions call people who have lived exceptionally good lives in the service of their religion 'saints'.

For example, the founder of Sikhism, Guru Nanak, is thought of by many as a saint. In Judaism, especially spiritual people are called *tzadik*, or 'righteous ones', and they are similar to saints. The Catholic Church has many saints, such as St Bernadette, who is said to have seen visions of Mary, the mother of Jesus, at Lourdes in France.

However, some argue that every human being is a mixture of good and bad and that it is wrong to imagine that some people are saints, meaning that they are purer than other people.

Before we decide if we might be better off without saints, we should try to understand *why* they are around. Can they be helpful role models for believers? Even if you don't believe that one person can be so much better than anyone else, you might still be able to learn something useful from the lives of saints.

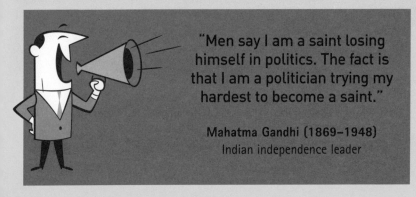

"Men say I am a saint losing himself in politics. The fact is that I am a politician trying my hardest to become a saint."

Mahatma Gandhi (1869–1948)
Indian independence leader

DO RELIGIONS HELP THE POOR?

Almost every religion teaches that we have a duty to help the poor. One of the five 'Pillars of Islam' – the things you must do to be a good Muslim – is to pay *zakaah*, a gift of money for the poor and needy. Jesus also taught, "The person who has two coats must share with the one who doesn't have any, and the person who has food, must do the same."

Today and throughout history, religious groups have spent a great deal of money building temples, churches and other places of worship.

Do you think that money would have been better spent going directly to the poor and needy? Or do you think that these temples and churches have helped poor people in some way?

Most religions put money and effort into helping the poor, but you don't need to be religious to give to charity. Anyone can try to be a compassionate and good person, whatever their beliefs.

WHAT DO RELIGIONS SAY ABOUT ANIMALS?

In some religions, such as Christianity, Judaism and Islam, animals are put on Earth by God for our benefit. We should look after them and not treat them cruelly, but, many argue, *they do not have souls as we do*. Animals do not go to heaven or hell.

Some of these religions have rules about what animals we are allowed to eat, but this is because some meat is said to be 'unclean', not because particular animals should be respected.

In religions such as Buddhism, Hinduism and Jainism, however, there is not a big difference between humans and animals. Followers believe that souls can live in different bodies in different lives. *The soul of a cat in this life may be the soul of a person in the future.*

In the Hindu holy book the Mahabharata, it says, "He who desires to increase his own flesh by eating the flesh of other creatures lives in misery in whatever species he may take his birth."

DO RELIGIONS TREAT MEN and WOMEN THE SAME?

In most religions, men are given more power than women. In the Roman Catholic Church, for example, *only men* can be priests, bishops or Pope, the head of the church. In Islam, *only men* can be full imams, able to lead the whole mosque in prayer. In Buddhism, almost every *tulku* or *lama* – leaders who are said to have lived past lives – are *men*.

These religions say that although men and women are treated differently, they are still equal. Men are not better than women, but they are better suited to some roles in the religion.

However, critics say that men and women are *not* treated equally because men have more powerful positions.

In recent years, many people inside and outside religion have challenged the different treatment of men and women. In the Anglican tradition of Christianity, for example, women can now be priests and there are plans to allow them to be bishops too. Some of the biggest arguments in religion today are about the role of women.

In many cultures, women are expected to cover up their bodies more than men. It's thought to be wrong for women to appear attractive to men other than their husbands.

The Koran, the holy book of Islam, says that women should dress 'modestly', but Muslims disagree about how to interpret this. Some think this means not wearing short skirts or skimpy tops, but some believe a woman should wear a headscarf to cover her hair in public. Others believe she must also wear a *niqab* (face veil) or *burqa*, a loose robe that covers her whole body including her head.

For devout Muslims, this is a question of how to understand the teachings of the Koran. But for others, it is an example of how women are not treated the same as men. *Why should women be obliged to follow stricter rules for dressing than men?*

And is it entirely up to Muslims to decide how Muslim women dress? Is it solely a matter for Catholics to decide whether a woman could be Pope? *What do you think?*

DOES RELIGION

One of the biggest criticisms of religion is that it causes wars. Throughout history, there have been many conflicts between religions, or different groups of the same religion.

For example, between the 11th and 13th centuries, 'the Crusades' saw Christian knights from European armies do battle against Muslims in the Holy Land, an area now occupied by Lebanon, Syria, Palestine, Israel and Egypt. In Ireland in the 20th century, there were many conflicts between Protestant and Catholic Christians.

And more than 20 million people died in China between 1850 and 1864, when Hong Xiuquan and his army attempted to replace Taoism, Confucianism and Buddhism with his own form of Christianity.

CAUSE WAR?

But are these wars *only* about religion? *Perhaps they are more about power, money and occupying land.* Are the wars actually *political* rather than *religious?*

And some of the biggest wars in history have not been about religion at all. World War I (1914–1918) was fought mainly between Christian countries and was not about religion. World War II (1939–1945) was more of a fight between political views – communism, fascism and democracy – than it was about religion.

It is true that religion *can* cause war, when tensions between different religious groups become too much. But it does not seem that religion is the *main cause* of war. Most wars have *political causes*. They are about who has power and who controls land, *not* who has the right religion.

IS THERE A HEAVEN?

We've seen that religious people believe different things. But almost every single one has some idea of 'heaven'. The idea is that, after this life, there is another life in *a different, better place* – for good people, at least.

Some of these ideas can get very complicated. In Hinduism, for example, there isn't just one heaven. Rather there are *several different heavenly levels*.

You could argue that heaven is more important than Earth. On Earth, people live for an average of about 70 years. But many religions tell us we can live *forever* in heaven.

In fact, heaven sounds like a good idea in many ways. We get to live forever (so dying is not so scary) in a really nice place! *Is that why some people believe in heaven?*

But does heaven really exist? It doesn't seem fair to grant some people eternal life and not others, when different people are given very different opportunities in life to prove that they are worthy and good.

More important, perhaps, is that we seem to be animals of some kind. Remember, we are related to chimpanzees! But if we are animals, *how could we live forever after our bodies have died?*

IS THERE A HELL?

If there is a heaven, does that mean there is also a 'hell'? Again, most religions have said that not only do the good go to heaven, but the wicked go to hell, where they are punished for *all eternity*. Inside many churches, you'll see a painting of the Last Judgement, which shows the good entering heaven and the bad being condemned to hell.

Many find the idea of hell harder to believe than heaven. If God is good, *why would he punish anyone for all eternity?* Surely no one is so bad that they deserve such punishment?

WHAT IS THE DEVIL?

If you think of hell, you'll probably think of the man in charge: the 'devil', or 'Satan'. In Christianity, Judaism and Islam, Satan was originally an *angel*, but he disobeyed God and was cast out of heaven. He's been tempting people to be evil ever since.

In other religions, there is no person or fallen angel such as the devil. Instead, there are *two opposing forces* – good and evil.

So does the devil really exist? Although some people think he does, most religious people now think of Satan as an *image* of evil, rather than a real person.

The devil represents the temptation to do evil and to refuse God's will. He is not a real creature with horns and a forked tail!

WHY WOULD GOD ALLOW EVIL?

Here's a puzzle: if God is all-powerful, all-knowing and all-good, *why is there so much evil and suffering in the world?* Why are there nasty diseases and why do earthquakes and other natural disasters destroy lives? Why are people allowed to do horrible things to each other all the time?

It seems that God either *doesn't want* to stop these things happening (so he's not all-good) or he *can't* stop them (so he's not all-powerful). Whichever way you look at it, it would mean that *God is not what we think he is – or perhaps he doesn't exist at all.*

Some people think they have an answer to this. They say that there are very important reasons why God must allow these things to happen. Somehow, in some way, it is better for human beings that terrible things happen. Perhaps we need bad things to give us the opportunity to do good in response. Maybe we need to learn the difference between right and wrong, and that means we have to see some very wrong things for ourselves.

Is that a good enough answer? People disagree. But most agree that *the existence of terrible things in the world is not easy to explain if a good God is in charge.*

IS GOD EVER WRONG?

Maybe bad things happen because God makes mistakes. *Is that possible?*

In ancient Greece, the gods were often shown to be quite human – they could be childish, grumpy, envious, mean, spiteful and mischievous – and they would sometimes get things wrong.

But most of the time, God is thought to be perfect. And if he's perfect, he can't possibly make any mistakes.

So if God *is* ever wrong, *he's not God as we know him!*

COULD GOD BE WICKED?

Here's a worrying possibility: could it be that the reason why there is so much evil in the world is because God *isn't* good after all? *Could the Universe be ruled by a wicked God?*

Since we don't really know for sure what God is like, or even if he exists, this is a possibility. But it doesn't look very likely. As well as suffering and pain, there are so many *good* things in the world, so much happiness, joy and love. A wicked God would surely not allow so many wonderful things to exist in his creation!

So even if there is no good God, it seems even *less likely* that there's a wicked one.

4

LIVING WITH FAITH, GOD, SOULS AND ANGELS

Some people don't take their religion too seriously. If you ask them what their religion is, they might say "Christian" or "Hindu", but most of the time they wouldn't even think about it.

However, for people who *do* take religion seriously, it can affect *every area of their lives*. Living a religious life can be very different to living a non-religious one.

For some people, their religion is *so important* that they give up ordinary life and dedicate all their time to prayer and serving God in small groups. Women who do this are called 'nuns' and they live together in buildings called 'convents'. Men who do the same are called 'monks' and they live in 'monasteries'. They wear the same simple clothes as each other and do not own anything. They do not get married or have children.

It's time to look at some of the things that really matter in the lives of truly religious people, to see what difference it makes to have *faith*.

WHAT IS FAITH?

There's a famous story about *faith* that is told by Jews, Christians and Muslims. Abraham, an important prophet in all three religions, wanted a child for years, but he and his wife, Sarah, could not have one. Then God made sure she got pregnant, and she had a son, Isaac.

A few years later, an angel appeared to Abraham and told him that God wanted him to *sacrifice* Isaac – *to kill him as a gift to God*. Although Isaac was the most important thing in the world to Abraham, and although he would never usually kill a person, he decided to follow God's command. But at the last minute, an angel stopped him, saying that Abraham had done enough to prove his faith in God. Isaac was saved.

The story shows that Abraham had tremendous faith in God. Faith is more than just belief – *it is a kind of trusting in God that does not ask for any explanation*. Abraham did not question, he just accepted, even though what he was asked to do appeared to be terrible. Many religious people think this is what we should all do – trust in our religious beliefs, and our God or gods, without asking for an explanation.

Some people think, however, that faith is a *bad thing*. They think that we should always rely on *reason and explanation* before we believe something, and we should not just do whatever religion asks us to do, especially if it seems wrong. With this view, Abraham was *not* a hero, he was a fool. He should never have agreed to kill his only son.

So is faith a good or a bad thing? People disagree, and you have to decide for yourself.

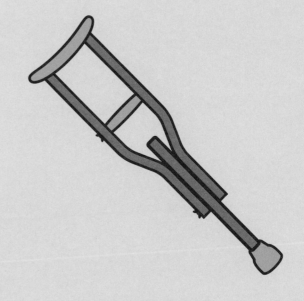

CAN FAITH HEAL PEOPLE?

Some people claim that *faith alone can heal*. If they pray and trust God, people can be healed of all sorts of illnesses.

Although there are many stories of people being miraculously cured in this way, there is no *definite proof* that any of them are *true*. People often get better for reasons we don't understand, so it is impossible to say if faith ever plays a part in healing.

So if you believe in faith healing, you do so as a matter of *faith*, not proof!

WHY DO PEOPLE WORSHIP?

Many religions include regular rituals of worship in which people praise and thank God. But *why* do they do this? And why would God want people to tell him how great he is?

One reason might be that it is important that we remain humble, meaning that we do not get too big for our boots. And praising God could help us think about *why* he is great and how we can become better people ourselves.

Another reason is that worship could be a way of reminding ourselves that we depend on God and should make him the centre of our lives.

Some worship, however, is harder to explain. In some parts of the world, people sacrifice animals to God, killing them as a gift. And sometimes, during the Hindu festival of Thaipusam, worshippers pierce their face and bodies with skewers or hooks as a sign of their devotion!

Unless you share these beliefs, it can be hard to imagine why any god would want his followers to carry out such extreme forms of worship.

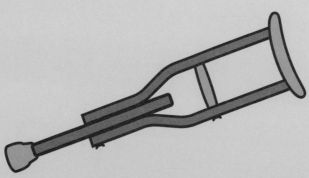

"Prayer does not change God, but it does change the one who prays."

Søren Kierkegaard (1813–1855)
Danish philosopher

HOW CAN WE TALK TO GOD?

Almost everyone agrees that God does not talk *directly* to people – at least not like someone talks to you on the telephone. *So how does he tell people what he wants?*

Most religions believe that in the past, God sent prophets, human beings who were given some special knowledge of God's desires to pass on to others. Religions also have their holy books, which many believe contain God's words.

But what about *now*? Is there anyone on Earth who speaks for God today?

Almost every religion has *leaders*, but hardly any of these people claim to have a *direct* communication with God. And there is certainly not a person alive who everyone would agree can speak on God's behalf.

So although there are people who try to understand and teach what they *think* God wants, no one can claim to speak for God.

WHAT IS AN ANGEL?

Many religions have stories about messengers from God being sent to Earth. These are often 'angels'. Angels are like people, but they live in heaven, not on Earth. They not only bring messages, they sometimes help people too.

But are angels real and did any of these appearances actually happen? As usual, people disagree. And even religious people disagree among themselves.

Although some people with faith believe in angels, others think they are just stories. So you don't have to believe in angels to be religious.

(And you don't need religion to believe in angels. But you might need some evidence!)

CAN THE VIRGIN MARY REALLY APPEAR IN A GRILLED CHEESE SANDWICH?

Angels aren't the only kinds of visitors from heaven. There are reports of other important religious figures appearing to people. For example, according to the Roman Catholic Church, the Virgin Mary, the mother of Jesus, has visited people in many places all over the world.

And in Sri Lanka, some Muslims believe that a satellite image of the 2004 tsunami, which killed hundreds of thousands of people, spells out the name of God, Allah. They think this means that God was punishing people for not being good enough Muslims.

Strangely, other people have reported seeing images of holy people or writings on walls and fences, cinnamon buns and chapattis, the branches of trees, frying pans and even on the fleece of a lamb! And in 2004, an American woman sold a ten-year-old grilled cheese sandwich for $28,000, because she and others believed it showed the image of the Virgin Mary.

To non-believers – and many believers too – all this is hard to accept. You can see all sorts of images and words in random shapes if you want to. Just spend half an hour looking at the clouds. How many things can you see in them? Does that mean *God* put them there?

CAN A TOOTH REALLY BE HOLY?

People often worship or pray at special places, such as temples, churches and mosques. These are *holy places*, meaning that they have a special connection with God or the spiritual world, and so they need to be treated with extra respect.

In some religions, *objects* said to have been touched or owned by holy people in the past are also considered to be holy. A saint's glove or book would be such an object, also called a 'relic'. One of the holiest relics in the world is in Sri Lanka. It is a tooth said to have been Buddha's.

This idea is not always used for good purposes. In the Middle Ages, for example, people used to make a lot of money selling what they claimed to be the bones of saints, when really they were just old animal bones.

Whether or not such religious objects are genuine, many people today think that the whole idea of holy places and holy things is old-fashioned. Holiness is nothing to do with *physical objects*, they might say. You can have faith and connect with God simply by thinking about him – *wherever you are and without the need for a 'prop'*.

If you are religious, only you can decide if places and objects are holy and how important they are to your faith.

SHOULD CHILDREN INHERIT RELIGION?

Most people who are religious bring up their children to be part of the *same religion*. It's obvious why – their religion is important to them and they want their children to benefit from it in the ways that they do. And perhaps they inherited the religion from *their own parents*.

But some people argue that it is *wrong* to bring up children in a particular religion. They think that everyone should be able to decide *for themselves* what is true. If you teach children just one religion, you are *brainwashing* them. Why promote one particular religion when you think it is wrong to encourage children to have one particular view about politics?

Another view is that children should be encouraged to *think for themselves*, learning about different religious and non-religious ways of life. However, it is fine if their parents spend more time teaching them about their own faith rather than about other beliefs.

So which view is right? *How should you be brought up?* Should you *inherit* religion from your parents or should you work it out for yourself?

CAN A BABY HAVE A RELIGION?

Here's a puzzle: in many religions, there is a ceremony to welcome a baby into a particular religion. In Christianity, that ceremony is *baptism*.

But a baby cannot even talk and has no opinions about God or religion. So in what way can it make sense to say that a baby is Christian – or Jewish or Sikh? What could it mean to say a baby belongs to a particular religion?

Does a person need to be able to think for him or herself in order to belong to a religion?

BRAIN BURN!

If a baby is baptized as a Christian but then adopted by devout Taoist parents, what religion does that baby belong to?

DO I HAVE A SOUL?

Who are you? *What* are you?

Take a look at yourself. What makes you *you?* You have a body and you have a brain. But what would happen if we *took away* your body and brain? *Would there be any of you left?*

Some people say the answer is *yes.* As well as your physical body and brain, you have a *soul,* which is not physical. It may live in your body for now, but when your body dies, your soul could live on, perhaps in heaven.

In many branches of Christianity, a soul cannot live separately from a body. Heaven involves the body coming back *physically,* just as Jesus was resurrected with a body. We do have a soul, but it is in some way part of our body.

In Hinduism, it is the soul that is the *real nature* of a person, rather than the body. This soul, or spirit, is called *atman*, and it is a Hindu's goal in life to discover his or her true self as atman and to realize oneness with Brahman, the Ultimate Reality.

Most people who are not religious do not believe in souls. They think that we are very complex animals and that when our bodies die, *we* do too.

The question of whether we have souls turns out not only to be a very, very big one, but also a very, very complicated one. Even if we *do* have souls, most people would say that it does not mean the real you is like a *ghost* inside your body.

So if there *are* souls, what are they *made of? Where* are they? How do they separate themselves from our bodies?

CAN I PICK AND CHOOSE FROM RELIGION?

We've seen that there are many religions and many different things that people believe, even when they share the same religion. So is it possible to take just what you like from different religions, believing some things and rejecting others?

In a way, most religious people do a bit of this anyway. There is never complete agreement between members of a church, for example, even among the leaders. So people often pick and choose the bits of their religion they believe in.

But at the same time, you can't just pick the bits *you like the sound of*. The question you should ask is *what bits are true*? And then you have to ask whether the bits you think are true *fit together*. For example, you can't believe that Jesus is the son of God and also believe that the Prophet Mohammed revealed the word of God – because Mohammed said that Jesus was *not* the son of God.

So you can decide for yourself what, if anything, you believe. But you need to have a *reason* for believing what you do. You need to think hard about what is true.

CAN I CHANGE MY RELIGION?

The religion most people have is the one they are brought up with, the one they 'inherit' from their family and cultural background.

But if you decide a different religion is better, you can change. This is called 'conversion' – because you *convert* from one religion to another.

How easy this is depends on the religion. It also depends on how important religion is to your family or community. It can be very hard to change religion if everyone around you thinks it is important that you don't.

Whatever you decide, *it is a big decision*, one you should think hard about before making.

SO WHAT SHOULD I BELIEVE?

You must know the answer to this question by now! There is so much disagreement about religion that *no one can tell you what you should believe*. People may have strong opinions, but these opinions differ, so *only you* can decide who or what you think is right.

You might decide not to believe in any religion at all and be an *atheist*. Many, many people live happily and well without religion.

Other people, called *agnostics*, say that they just do not know what is true and they live with this uncertainty. They keep an open mind and continue to ask questions, accepting that they may have no answers.

Whether you are a believer, an agnostic or atheist is entirely down to you. Whatever you decide, you should at least now have some idea of how religion and faith pose many, many questions. Your lifetime of exploring and investigating those questions and, most importantly, *thinking for yourself,* has only just begun!

GLOSSARY

Words in **bold** refer to other glossary entries.

AGNOSTICISM A belief system asserting that it is not known if **God** exists or not and that an open mind should be kept about it.

ANCIENT GREEK RELIGION The **religion** of Greece centuries before the time of **Jesus**. There were different **gods** for different things. For example, Athena was the goddess of wisdom and Poseidon was the god of the sea.

ANGEL A spiritual being who is sometimes sent by **God** to Earth as a messenger or protector.

ANIMISM A belief system asserting that all animals, plants and objects have **souls**.

ATHEISM A belief system asserting that there is no **God** or **gods**.

BAPTISM A Christian ceremony in which a baby, child or adult is sprinkled or covered with water and welcomed as a member of the **religion**.

BIBLE The Hebrew Bible is the **holy** book of **Judaism**. Christians call this the Old Testament, and together with their New Testament, it forms the Christian Bible. Both bibles are collections of many shorter books.

BIG BANG The massive explosion that scientists believe brought our **Universe** into existence. The Big Bang took place about 13 billion years ago.

BISHOP A high-ranking priest in the Christian **church**. The head of some churches is called the Archbishop.

BUDDHISM A **religion**, which grew largely in India and southeast Asia, that focuses on the spiritual development of the individual rather than the **worship** of **gods**. It is the fourth-largest **religion** in the world.

CHRISTIANITY The largest **religion** in the world. Christians believe that **Jesus** Christ is the son of **God**, and that he was sent to Earth to take away the **sins** of the world.

CHURCH A building in which Christians meet to **worship** or a particular group of Christians, such as the Church of England.

COMMUNION A Christian ceremony in which people consume bread and wine, which symbolize the body and blood of **Jesus**.

CONFUCIANISM An ancient Chinese philosophy that some consider to be a **religion** because it involves **rituals** and the **worship** of ancestors. Humanity and loyalty are among its most important values.

DEITY A god or goddess, usually assuming human or animal form.

FAITH Belief that is based on trust rather than proof or strong evidence.

GOD Usually a supernatural being who created and controls the **Universe**, including life on Earth.

GODS Supernatural beings who are each responsible for different aspects of human, animal and natural life.

HEAVEN A place where good people who have obeyed **God** are believed to live forever after death.

HELL A place of punishment where wicked people who have disobeyed **God** in their lifetime are believed to be sent after death.

HINDUISM A **religion**, the third largest in the world, originating along the Indus Valley in what is modern-day Pakistan. Hindus believe their real nature to be a **spirit** called *atman* and they strive to achieve unity with Brahman, the Ultimate Reality. Hinduism has thousands of **gods**, or **deities**, who can help believers find their pathway to Brahman, their one true **God**.

HOLY Spiritually pure, sacred.

IMAM A leader of a **mosque** or **Muslim** community.

ISLAM A **religion** that rose in the 7th century CE under the leadership of the **Prophet Mohammed** in what is now Saudi Arabia. It is the second-largest and fastest-growing **religion** in the world.

JAINISM One of the oldest surviving belief systems in the world, Jainism is an Indian **religion** that emphasizes respect for all life, even the smallest insects, and the need to free the **soul** from the body.

JESUS A man who lived 2,000 years ago in what is now Israel. Christians believe Jesus, or Jesus Christ, is the son of **God** and that he was sent to Earth to take away the **sins** of the world.

JEW A person can be a Jew by being born to a Jewish mother or by joining the **religion** of **Judaism**. Many people call themselves Jews because their ancestors were Jewish, not because they follow **Judaism** as a **religion**.

JUDAISM Originating with the **prophet** Abraham in the Middle East, Judaism is the **religion** of the Jewish people, who, according to the **Bible**, were chosen by **God**.

KORAN Often written Qur'an, the **holy** book of **Islam** said to be the direct word of **God**, which came to the **Prophet Mohammed** through the archangel Jibril (Gabriel) between 610–632CE.

MEDITATION A spiritual practice in which people try to become aware of their true nature or the nature of **God**. Meditation is common in the **religions** of **Buddhism**, **Hinduism** and **Sikhism**.

MOSQUE A building in which **Muslims** meet to **worship**.

MUSLIM A follower of **Islam**.

PHILOSOPHER A person who thinks carefully and seriously about questions that don't have factual answers, such as *How should we live?* and *What is knowledge?*

PLATO One of the greatest **philosophers** in history, Plato lived in ancient Greece. His ideas about the difference between mind (or **soul**) and body influenced Christian and non-religious thought for centuries.

POLITICAL Relating to the decisions and interests of the governments and rulers of different countries or groups of people.

PRAY To talk to **God** in some way, usually by asking him for help or guidance, or by **worshipping** or thanking him.

PRIEST A leader of a **church** or Christian community.

PROPHET A person to whom it is said that **God** has given special knowledge. The prophet can then pass on God's message to others.

PROPHET MOHAMMED Mohammed is usually called the founder of **Islam**. **Muslims** believe his task was to restore the true **religion** of **prophets** such as Adam, Noah, Abraham, Moses and **Jesus**.

RABBI A Jewish religious teacher, often the leader of a **synagogue** or Jewish community.

REASON The human capacity to think through ideas, relying as little as possible on hunches, intuitions or people who claim to already know the answers.

RELIGION An organized system of belief that involves some kind of acceptance of a reality beyond the physical world that we see around us.

RESURRECTED Brought back to life.

RITUAL A repeated series of actions that are often part of a religious ceremony.

ROMAN CATHOLICISM A major branch of **Christianity** that traces its roots back to the first followers of **Jesus**. Its head is the Pope and its headquarters is Vatican City, an independent city state in Rome, Italy.

SCIENCE An attempt to understand how the world works by experiment, measurement and observation.

SIKHISM The fifth-largest **religion** in the world, founded in 15th-century India by Guru Nanak. Followers use **meditation** to attempt to achieve a spiritual union with **God**.

SIN Something that breaks the law of **God**.

SOUL The part of a person that is believed to be separate from the body and, some say, can live on after the body has died.

SPIRIT A being or power that is not physical.

SYNAGOGUE A building in which **Jews** meet to **worship**.

TAOISM A Chinese religious and philosophical system (sometimes written as 'Daoism') that is concerned with living in harmony with the natural energy of the **Universe**.

TEMPLE A religious building in which believers meet to **worship**. Followers of **Buddhism** and **Hinduism** **pray** in temples.

TORAH Five books containing the major texts of Jewish religious law. The first five books of both the Jewish and Christian **Bible** are: Genesis, Exodus, Leviticus, Numbers and Deuteronomy.

UNITED NATIONS An international organization to which almost all of the world's governments belong. The UN tries to help countries experiencing difficulties due to war, poverty or natural disaster.

UNIVERSE The entire physical world, containing all the planets, all the stars and all of space and time.

WORSHIP Praising and giving thanks to **God** or **gods**.

INDEX

FURTHER READING

BOOKS

Really, Really Big Questions about life, the Universe and everything – Stephen Law

Really, Really Big Questions about Space and Time – Mark Brake

The Philosophy Files – Stephen Law

The Philosophy Files 2 – Stephen Law

What Do You Believe? – Aled Jones

WEBSITES

World religions:
www.bbc.co.uk/religion/religions

Facts and figures about religions:
www.religionfacts.com

Camp Quest:
www.camp-quest.org.uk

Critical thinking fun:
www.skeptic.com/junior_skeptic

HOW TO THINK & ASK QUESTIONS

Don't just ask *what* people believe, think about *why* they believe it. Here are three useful *why* questions:

1. *Why do people want to believe some things and not others?* Think about their *motives*. Ideas are not just true or false – they can be appealing or unappealing. If we really want something to be true, then we might believe it, even if it's false.

2. *Why should we believe the things that religious and non-religious people believe are true?* Think about the *reasons* and *evidence* for different beliefs. What *good reasons* can someone give to show that their holy book is the word of God? What *evidence* does another person have for saying that God doesn't exist?

3. *Why do people belong to a particular religion?* It's not always about belief or what is true. People might belong to a religion to be a member of the same group as their family or others from their country.